Tugs and Offshore Supply Vessels

2006/07

(UK and Ireland)

by

James Dodds

Introduction

For several years, there was a demand for a listing of tugs and offshore supply ships to be seen in ports and coastal locations around the UK. Two years ago, this demand was met with the publication of the first edition of *Tugs and Offshore Supply Vessels - UK*. That booklet soon sold out prompting the need for this updated and expanded edition. Once again, much thought has been given to which vessels should be included. In the supply ships section will be found some vessels which have been converted from a supply function to essentially standby vessels. The tug section includes some vessels known as multicats which are essentially workboats but with a towing capacity. Feedback from readers of the first edition has enabled me to decide which vessels to include. Further feedback will be much appreciated.

As with all such lists of ships, no guarantee is given about the accuracy of the figures which should be considered merely as a guideline. Every effort has been made to obtain correct figures but there is sometimes disagreement among the main sources. We have tended to use figures given in *Lloyd's Register of Shipping* where these are available. For very new vessels, little information other than a name is available but some of these have been included in the fleets. Information has been corrected to the end of July 2005. The main heading for each company indicates its role as operator, owner or manager.

The details for each vessel are as follows
Column 1   Name (& flag for supply ships, followed by former names)
Column 2   Year of build
Column 3   Gross tonnage
Column 4   Length overall
Column 5   Beam
Column 6   Draught
Column 7   Horsepower
Column 8   Bollard pull ahead (n/a means not available or not applicable)

I wish to thank all the companies which have responded to requests for information, the vast majority of those listed having done so. I also wish to thank my father for his help, Dominic and Bernard McCall who have added further information, and Gilbert Mayes who has checked many details. Mention must also be made of Danny Lynch and Chris Jones who have given considerable assistance. Thanks also to the staff at Sebright Printers for their excellent work.

Despite our best efforts, the book may contain errors. Users of the book who have further information about any of the vessels listed are invited to contact me via the publisher.

James Dodds   Aberdeen, July 2005

Published by Bernard McCall, 400 Nore Road, Portishead, Bristol, BS20 8EZ, England.
Website : www.coastalshipping.co.uk
Telephone/fax : 01275 846178. E-mail : bernard@coastalshipping.co.uk
All distribution enquiries should be addressed to the publisher.

Printed by Sebright Printers, 12 - 18 Stokes Croft, Bristol, BS1 3PR
Telephone : 0117 942 5827; fax : 0117 942 0671;
e-mail : info@sebright.co.uk; website : www.sebright.co.uk

ISBN : 1-902953-19-3

*Front cover : The **Battleaxe** underway at Port Talbot on 1 February 2005.*

(Dominic McCall)

OFFSHORE VESSELS

BOSTON PUTFORD OFFSHORE SAFETY LTD

Columbus Buildings, Waveney Road, Lowestoft, Suffolk, NR31 1BS
Tel : 01502 573366   Fax : 01502 581500
Website : www.seacormarine.com
Livery - Dark orange hull, white upperworks; black funnel with red S logo.

Name		Year							
NOVA (GBR)	1969	715	54,30	11,43	4,19	2400	33.00
PUTFORD ACHATES (GBR)	1976	1043	53,60	11,79	3,84	2400	n/a
(ex Maersk Tanis-89, Bin Jabr 1-87, Maersk Leader-83)							
PUTFORD ACHILLES (GBR)	1973	1179	58,27	13,14	5,10	4198	n/a
(ex Auriga Tide-90, Vivien Tide-84, Lady Vivien-74)							
PUTFORD AJAX (GBR)	1976	1043	53,60	11,79	3,84	2400	n/a
(ex Maersk Tanta-89, Bin Jabr 2-87, Maersk Logger-83)							
PUTFORD APOLLO (GBR)	1975	868	56,32	11,03	4,55		n/a
(ex Mansal-89, Mohamed-87, Rig Mate-79)							
PUTFORD ARIES (GBR)	1977	1829	66,93	14,56	4,75	4800	n/a
(ex Stirling Aries-96, Star Aries-96)							
PUTFORD ARTEMIS (GBR)	1975	1190	58,85	12,02	4,81	6001	n/a
(ex Coral Sea 2-92, Moon Lady-90, Aomjai III-90, Selco Supply 1-87, Ibis Five-80)							
PUTFORD ATHENA (GBR)	1975	1188	58,24	12,03	4,14	6161	n/a
(ex Severn Mariner-92, Siddis Mariner-90)							
PUTFORD ENTERPRISE (GBR)	1985	1793	68,33	15,80	5,21	5000	n/a
(ex Stirling Altair-02, Star Altair-96)							
PUTFORD GUARDIAN (GBR)	1967	638	50,81	11,26	3,79	2001	n/a
(ex Essex Service-84, Essex Shore-80)							
PUTFORD PROTECTOR (GBR)	1983	1822	68,46	16,18	5,21	4970	n/a
(ex Stirling Capella-02, Star Capella-96)							
PUTFORD PROVIDER (GBR)	1983	1737	68,46	16,18	5,21	4970	n/a
(ex Stirling Vega-02, Star Vega-96)							
PUTFORD PUFFIN (GBR)	1970/91	661	45,57	11,82	3,20		
(ex Dawn Patrol-94, Barracuda-91, Smit Barracuda-87)							
PUTFORD ROVER (GBR)	1982	1294	64,39	13,82	5,23	1441	n/a
(ex Al Mojil XXXIV-96, Gryphaea-93, Agip Gryphaea-89)							
PUTFORD SHORE (GBR)	1967	638	48,77	10,60	3,81	1599	n/a
(ex Dawn Shore-94, Norfolk Service-84, Norfolk Shore-81)							
PUTFORD TERMINATOR (IOM)	1986	1399	65,21	14,64	5,29	5600	n/a
(ex Stirling Esk-04)							
PUTFORD TRADER (GBR)	1976	1329	57,50	13,01	5,10	4200	n/a
(ex Safe Truck-95, Seaway Jura-90)							
PUTFORD VIKING (GBR)	1976	1492	60,99	14,56	4,76	4800	n/a
(ex Blue Flame 1-00, Star Pegasus-87)							

PUTFORD
VOYAGER (GBR)   1985   1510   64,62   14,23   5,40   4800   n/a
(ex Stirling Dee-02)
PUTFORD WORKER (GBR) 1976 1417   65,52   14,00   5,92   3200
TYPHOON (CYM)   1976   936   56,39   11,61   3,81   2250   n/a
(ex Java Seal-91)
Offshore services in the North Sea
Part of the Seacor Group

The *PUTFORD TERMINATOR* arrives at Great Yarmouth.

(Paul Gowen)

BP SHIPPING LTD
Farburn Industrial Estate, Dyce, Aberdeen, AB2 0PB
Tel : 01224 834836   Fax : 01224 834890
Website : www.bp.com
CALEDONIAN
VANGUARD (IOM)   2006   5450   93,45   22,00   6,50
CALEDONIAN
VICTORY (IOM)   2006   5450   93,45   22,00   6,50
CALEDONIAN
VIGILANCE (IOM)   2007   5450   93,45   22,00   6,50
CALEDONIAN
VISION (IOM)   2007   5450   93,45   22,00   6,50
CALEDONIAN (tbn) (IOM) 2006 5450 93,45   22,00   6,50
Offshore services in the North Sea

BUE MARINE LTD
Imperial House, Albert Dock, Leith, EH6 7DN
Tel : 0131 554 9456   Fax : 0131 554 8328
E-mail : reception@bue.co.uk
Website : www.buemarine.com
Livery - Dark blue hull with white housing; white funnel with company logo

CASTLE	(CYM)	1999	1969	67,00	16,00	5,91	5448	

(ex Waveney Castle-03)

ISLAY	(AZE)	2002	2544	73,80	16,00	6,50	15000	167.0

(ex Stirling Islay-03)

JURA	(AZE)	2002	2544	73,80	16,00	6,50	15000	165.0

(ex Stirling Jura-03)

SWAN	(TKM)	1971	769	53,34	11,00	3,45	3800	
TULPAR	(KAZ)	2002	3343	94,08	21,00	3,96	8448	50.0

Managed for BUE Azerbaijan LLC

BARRA	(AZE)	1986	977	53,88	12,22	4,71	2022	n/a

(ex BUE Barra-03, Earl-99, Hornbeck Earl-86, Sunset Earl-95, Far Earl-93,
Seaforth Earl-89)

Managed for Kaspmorneftegazflot (Azerbaijan)

NEFTEGAZ 62	(AZE)	1988	2723	81,40	16,30	5,26	7200	80.0
NERCHA	(AZE)	1985	3861	67,30	13,90	5,20	7240	86.0
YARENGA	(AZE)	1984	1350	67,30	13,90	5,20	7150	86.0

Managed for Oil Industry Administration (Azerbaijan)

GULTAKIN								
ASKEROVA	(AZE)	1983	2723	81,30	16,30	7,20	7200	80.0

(ex Neftegaz 11-95)

IRGIZ	(AZE)	1983	583	50,47	11,60	4,26	3800	40.0
NEFTEGAZ 58	(AZE)	1990	2723	81,40	16,30	5,26	7200	80.0
NEFTEGAZ 64	(AZE)	1989	2723	81,40	16,30	5,26	7200	80.0
OM	(AZE)	1985	1585	67,30	13,90	5,20	7240	86.0

BUE VIKING LTD
11th Floor, Salvesen Tower, Blaikies Quay, Aberdeen
Tel : 01224 578750   Fax : 01224 578751
E-mail : info@bueviking.com
Website : www.bueviking.com
Livery - Dark blue hull with dark yellow stripe and dark yellow wheelhouse

BRITANNIA								
CONQUEST	(GBR)	1974	422	39,81	8,95	3,94	2000	25.0

(ex Suffolk Conquest-91)

BRITANNIA								
HARVESTER	(GBR)	1972	433	39,81	8,95	3,94	2000	25.0

(ex Suffolk Harvester-90, Venturer-84, Suffolk Harvester-79)

BRITANNIA								
MONARCH	(GBR)	1973	422	39,81	8,95	3,94	2000	25.0

(ex Suffolk Monarch-90, St David-84, Suffolk Monarch-78)

Name	Flag	Year						
BRITANNIA WARRIOR	(GBR)	1973	430	39,81	8,95	3,94	2000	25.0
(ex Suffolk Warrior-90)								
BUE ARRAN	(GBR)	1975	767	53,22	11,03	3,39	2300	n/a
(ex Scout-99, Hornbeck Scout-97, Seaboard Scout-95, Mansal 28-91, Issa-87, Auk Truck-82)								
BUE CANNA	(GBR)	1980	836	55,66	11,60	3,97	2480	n/a
(ex Sapphire Tide-99, Hornbeck Sapphire-95, Seaboard Sapphire-95, Sape-90)								
BUE IONA	(GBR)	1977	1444	61,00	14,30	5,13	4200	n/a
(ex Coral-99, Hornbeck Coral-97, Seaboard Coral-95, Boa Coral-92, Ocean Coral-90, Highland Piper 1-87, Highland Piper-87)								
BUE ISLAY	(GBR)	1985	928	53,00	12,00	4,50	3808	48.0
(ex Searcher-99, Hornbeck Searcher-96, Sunset Searcher-95, Far Searcher-93, Nuna-91)								
BUE JURA	(GBR)	1974	1092	59,67	13,04	4,47	5600	72.5
(ex Cromarty Tide-00, Cromarty Service-93, Cromarty Shore-81)								
BUE LISMORE	(IOM)	1986	977	53,85	12,22	4,71	2022	n/a
(ex Baronet-99, Hornbeck Baronet-96, Sunset Baronet-95, Far Baronet-93, Seaforth Baronet-89)								
BUE RAASAY	(GBR)	1983	1328	58,53	13,00	4,72	4240	n/a
(ex Norse Tide-99, Sira Supporter-96, Drive Supporter-85)								
BUE RONA	(GBR)	1974	910	60,97	11,59	3,91	3200	n/a
(ex Evans Tide-99, Venture Service-92)								
BUE SKYE	(GBR)	1968	1339	70,40	11,99	4,11	1500	n/a
(ex Tidewater Integrity-99, Hornbeck Integrity-98, Seaboard Integrity-95, St Jasper-85)								
BUE STAFFA	(GBR)	1974	1210	58,27	13,14	5,11	4200	n/a
(ex Alexandra Tide-99, Lady Alexandra-74)								
BUE TIREE	(GBR)	1977	863	55,60	11,61	3,97	2480	n/a
(ex Supreme-99, Hornbeck Supreme-96, Seaboard Supreme-95, Sapucala-90)								
SCOTT GUARDIAN	(GBR)	1993	1280	55,00	12,70	4,50	1920	25.0
SHETLAND SERVICE	(GBR)	1973	965	59,97	11,92	4,45	4000	58.0
(ex Shetland Shore-80)								
TRAFALGAR GUARDIAN	(GBR)	1994	1280	55,00	12,70	4,50	1920	33.5
VIKING CHALLENGER	(GBR)	1964	999	64,45	10,32	4,70	900	n/a
(ex Britannia Challenger-98, Britannia De Hoop-90, De Hoop-89)								
VIKING CRUSADER	(GBR)	1976	1176	58,98	12,60	4,15	6160	73.0
(ex Britannia Crusader-97, Pan Salvor-91, Gute Salvor-90, Normand Engineer-87)								
VIKING DEFENDER	(GBR)	1983	680	46,82	11,02	6,91	2688	n/a
(ex Cam Defender-95, Jagima-88)								
VIKING ENDEAVOUR	(GBR)	1975	1177	58,98	12,02	4,12	6160	76.0
(ex Britannia Endeavour-98, Pan Engineer-91, Wiberg Supplier-90, Karmoy Boy-87)								
VIKING GUARDIAN	(GBR)	1971	594	41,79	9,78	3,60	1900	n/a
(ex Cam Guardian-95, Luneda-85)								

The *VIKING CRUSADER* arrives at Aberdeen on 9 October 2004.

(David Dodds)

VIKING
PROTECTOR (GBR) 1983 673 46,82 11,60 6,91 2500 n/a
(ex Cam Protector-95, Sentry Hemne-87)
VIKING PROVIDER (GBR) 1999 2102 68,13 14,50 5,66 6526 n/a
VIKING RANGER (GBR) 1983 680 46,72 11,61 6,92 2330 30.0
(ex Cam Ranger-95, Sentinel Cathinka-88)
VIKING RETRIEVER (GBR) 1972 594 42,73 9,78 3,91 1900 n/a
(ex Cam Retriever-95, Irvana-85)
VIKING SEARCHER (GBR) 1971 594 47,07 9,78 3,91 1900 n/a
(ex Cam Searcher-96, Gavina-85)
VIKING SEEKER (GBR) 1968 780 46,28 10,24 4,84 1850 n/a
(ex Cam Seeker-95, Seaquest Valiant-86, F. T. Hewlett-86, Canso Dart-84,
Acadia Gannet-73)
VIKING SENTINEL (GBR) 1982 673 46,72 11,02 6,75 2330 30.0
(ex Cam Sentinel-95, Sentinel Maria-87)
VIKING
SUPPORTER (GBR) 1983 680 46,72 11,02 6,91 2330 30.0
(ex Cam Supporter-95, Sentinel Teresa-89)
VIKING VANGUARD (GBR) 1972 604 46,69 9,02 4,49 1200 n/a
(ex Cam Viking-95, Biggas-91)
VIKING VEDETTE (GBR) 1970 628 46,51 9,02 4,53 1500 n/a
(ex Cam Vedette-95, Gnupur-92, Asthor-88, Lofottral III-81)

VIKING VIGILANT (GBR)   1957   623   56,80   9,35   4,34   2300   n/a
(ex St Lucia-95, Cam Vigilant-93, Tem-89, Rescue K-84, Rescue Kim-84, Senja-82,
R~4-78)
VIKING VIPER (GBR)   1966   651   50,35   9,17   4,27   1560   n/a
(ex Cam Viper-95, Hallarklettur-92, Haja-74)
VIKING VISCOUNT (GBR)   1971   604   46,69   9,02   4,49   1200   n/a
(ex Cam Viscount-95, Raiti-91)
VIKING VIXEN (GBR)   1975   475   39,71   9,17   3,68   1650   n/a
(ex St Patrick-95, Gavina-89, St Patrick-86)
VIKING VOYAGER (GBR)   1957   601   56,80   9,35   4,34   2300   n/a
(ex Cam Voyager-95, Rescue Olav-91, Nordcap-82, R~2-65)
VIKING VULCAN (GBR)   1976   475   39,71   9,17   4,01   1650   n/a
(ex St Phillip-98, Kerry Kathleen-90, St Phillip-86)

Offshore services in the North Sea

As we go to press, we understand that all BUE-prefixed vessels are to be renamed with a Viking prefix.

CONOCO LTD

Tetney Oil Terminal, Tetney Lock Road,Tetney, Grimsby, DN36 5NX
Tel : 01472 814101   Fax : 01469 556246
Website : www.conocophillips.com
SPURN HAVEN II (GBR)   1979   654   49,80   11,60   3,39   1700

Marine services assisting large tankers off Tetney monobuoy in the Humber estuary
Now managed by Svitzer Marine

FARSTAD SHIPPING LTD

Farstad House, Badentoy Avenue, Badentoy Industrial Park, Porthlethen, Aberdeen,
AB12 4YB
Tel : 01224 784000   Fax : 01224 783340
E-mail : aberdeen@farstad.co.uk
Website : www.farstad.no
Livery - Signal red hull with large white 'F' and white housing and wheelhouse
FAR CENTURION (IOM)   1983   1971   67,72   15,88   6,45   13040   141.0
(ex Seaforth Centurion-89)
FAR SALTIRE (IOM)   2002   2600   73,60   16,80   6,10   16320   170.0
FAR SCOTIA (IOM)   2001   1989   67,00   16,00   5,90   5460   n/a
FAR SCOTSMAN (IOM)   1982   1948   67,47   17,33   6,09   6760   n/a
(ex Seaforth Monarch-89)
FAR SERVER (IOM)   1991   2610   81,90   18,00   4,97   6600   n/a
FAR SERVICE (IOM)   1995   3052   83,80   18,80   6,35   7200   n/a
FAR SPIRIT (IOM)   1983   2169   69,09   17,51   5,02   6120   n/a
(ex Loch Shuna-89, Far Spirit-87, Stad Spirit-86)
FAR SUPERIOR (IOM)   1990   2999   92,30   18,50   4,97   6600   n/a
FAR SUPPLIER (IOM)   1999   3009   82,85   19,05   6,33   6700   n/a
FAR SUPPORTER (IOM)   1996   2998   83,80   18,80   6,24   7200   n/a

FAR SWAN (IOM)	2001	3606	89,40	18,80	6,20	10800	n/a
FAR SWIFT (IOM)	2003	2401	71,80	16,00	6,00	5378	
FAR VISCOUNT (IOM)	1982	1219	62,54	13,56	5,01	3400	n/a
(ex Seaforth Viscount-89)							

Managed by Farstad Shipping (Indian Pacific) Pty (Australia)

FAR SKY (IOM)	1991	2285	73,60	16,40	5,60	14400	158.0

Offshore services worldwide

The FAR SCOTIA approaches Peterhead.

GULF OFFSHORE (NORTH SEA) LTD
184 - 192 Market Street, Aberdeen, AB11 5PQ
Tel : 01224 336000   Fax : 01224 336039
E-mail : steve.wilson@gulfoffshore.co.uk
Website : www.gulfmark.com
Livery - Dark blue hull with white housing; white funnel with company logo.
        Dark green hull with white housing (Rim. Napolitani vessels)
        Blue hull with cream housing; blue funnel (Waveney vessels)
CLWYD

SUPPORTER (GBR)	1984	2762	81,39	16,30	4,91	7200	90.0
(ex Neftegaz 12-96)							

HIGHLAND

BUGLER (GBR)	2003	2050	71,80	16,00	5,90	2725	n/a

HIGHLAND

CHAMPION (GBR)	1979	2501	80,77	18,04	4,32	4800	
(ex Balblair-93, Tender Champion--85)							

HIGHLAND CITADEL (GBR) (ex Waveney Citadel-04)	1979	2501	81,03	18,04	4,32	5460	n/a
HIGHLAND COURAGE (GBR)	2002	3160	80,00	18,00	6,60	16320	170.0
HIGHLAND DRUMMER (GBR)	1997	1969	67,00	16,00	5,91	5450	n/a
HIGHLAND EAGLE (GBR)	2003	2244	72,00	16,00	5,91	5460	n/a

The HIGHLAND EAGLE moves cautiously across the basin at Aberdeen on 5 May 2003.
(David Dodds)

HIGHLAND ENDURANCE (GBR)	2003	2900	79,90	18,00	6,60	16320	170.0
HIGHLAND FORTRESS (GBR)	2001	2244	71,80	16,00	5,90	5450	n/a
HIGHLAND LEGEND (GBR) (ex Wimpey Seawitch-90)	1986	1001	59,00	14,13	4,40	3589	n/a
HIGHLAND MONARCH (GBR)	2003		67,00	16,00	6,00	5460	n/a
HIGHLAND NAVIGATOR (GBR)	2002	3277	84,00	18,80	6,20	8836	n/a
HIGHLAND PATRIOT (GBR) (ex Stirling Fyne-01, Edda Fjord-94)	1982	2088	71,23	17,54	5,46	9606	n/a
HIGHLAND PIONEER (GBR) (ex Oceanic Pioneer-00, Lowland Pioneer-99, Balder Vigra-85)	1983	2099	68,51	17,84	4,90	5400	n/a

HIGHLAND PIPER (GBR)	1996	1969	67,00	16,80	5,90	5452	n/a
HIGHLAND PRIDE (GBR)	1992	2610	81,90	18,00	4,98	6602	n/a
HIGHLAND ROVER (GBR)	1998	2186	71,80	16,00	5,90	5460	n/a
HIGHLAND SPIRIT (GBR)	1998	1717	61,60	17,80	5,60	5954	n/a
HIGHLAND SPRITE (GBR)	1986	1199	59,00	14,13	4,40	3589	n/a
(ex Wimpey Seasprite-88)							
HIGHLAND STAR (GBR)	1990	2637	81,90	18,00	4,98	6602	n/a
(ex Far Malin-91)							
HIGHLAND VALOUR (GBR)	2003	2900	79,90	18,00	6,60	16320	170.0
HIGHLAND WARRIOR (GBR)	1981	2960	81,80	18,00	5,77	5300	n/a
(ex Atlantic Warrior-97, Wira Maju-91, Stad Flex-88)							
NORTH PRINCE (GBR)	1978	2342	78,87	15,24	6,45	6000	n/a
(ex Sun Prince-89, Falderntor-89)							
SAFE TRUCK (GBR)	1996	1969	67,00	16,00	5,91	5450	n/a
On bareboat charter from Rim Napolitana							
GARGANO (GBR)	2002	2244	72,00	16,00		5500	n/a
PORTOSALVO (GBR)	2005		72,00	16,00	6,35	5452	
On bareboat charter from Waveney Shipping plc							
WAVENEY CASTLE (GBR)	2003	2050	71,80	16,00	5,90	5460	n/a
WAVENEY FORTRESS (GBR)	1999	1969	67,00	16,00	5,90	5450	n/a

Offshore services in the North Sea and Irish Sea

The green-hulled GARGANO approaches Aberdeen on 10 October 2004.

(David Dodds)

HAVILA SUPPLY (UK) LTD

Havila House, 60 - 62 Marischal Street, Aberdeen, AB11 5AL
Tel : 01224 212159   Fax : 01224 211513
E-mail : office@havila.co.uk
Website : www.havila.no
Livery : Green hull with white housing and wheelhouse

HAVILA CLEVER	(GBR)	1975	1409	71,37	12,37	4,44	7040	150.0
(ex Kronbas-98, West Penguin-86, Atlantic Fosna-80, Edda Atlantic-76)								
HAVILA FAITH	(IOM)	1999	3017	82,85	19,02	6,35	6600	n/a
(ex Stirling Spey-05)								
HAVILA FAVOUR	(IOM)	1998	3017	82,85	19,02	6,35	6600	n/a
(ex Stirling Tay-05)								
HAVILA FORCE	(IOM)	2000	2528	73,80	16,29	6,50	15000	165.0
(ex Stirling Iona-05)								

The HAVILA FORCE had only recently been renamed and was just out of drydock as she arrived at Aberdeen on 6 February 2005. *(David Dodds)*

HAVILA SEA	(BHS)	1975/95	1499	61,20	13,86	5,10	4200	
(ex Emerald Bas-98, Emerald Sprite-92, Sprite-91, Edda Sprite-83)								
HAVILA SEARCHER	(BHS)	1975	1472	64,40	13,80	5,90	8000	105.0
(ex Rem Searcher-98, Plan Searcher-95, Pan Searcher-93, Far Searcher-90, Tender Searcher-87)								
HAVILA SKY	(GBR)	1957/85	579	56,74	9,35	4,50	2300	
(ex Rescue Kim-98, Kim-95, Rescue Kim-92, Andenes-84, R 5-65)								
HAVILA STAR	(BHS)	2000	1864	66,00	15,00	4,70	5434	60.0
HAVILA SUN	(BHS)	1972/95	1151	58,40	11,70	4,35	2880	
(ex Sunbas-98, Sun Tender-95, North Breeze-91, Ocean Range-90, Remberiturm-88)								
HAVILA TIGRIS	(BHS)	2001	1864	66,00	15,00	4,70	5435	60.0

Offshore services in the North Sea

KLYNE TUGS (LOWESTOFT) LTD

Cumberland Place, 4-6 Whapload Road, Lowestoft, Suffolk, NR32 1UQ
Tel : 01502 515250/565610   Fax : 01502 500225
E-mail : inquiries@klyne-tugs.demon.co.uk
Livery - Green hull with cream housing

| ANGLIAN EARL | (GBR) | 1987 | 2311 | 69,90 | 15,90 | 6,50 | 12000 | 150.0 |

(ex Maersk Logger-03)

Offshore services and relief work for MCA tugs (see page 48)

The ANGLIAN EARL approaches Lowestoft.

(Paul Gowen)

THE MAERSK COMPANY LTD

Portland House, Station Road, Ballasalla, Isle of Man, IM9 2RB
Tel : 01624 828100   Fax : 01624 822618
Website : www.maersksupply.com
Livery - Sky blue hull with cream housing; dark blue funnel, sky blue band with white star.

Managed for The Maersk Company Limited - Shipping Division

MAERSK								
ADVANCER	(IOM)	2004		90,30	23,00	7,80	23500	280.0
MAERSK								
ASSERTER	(IOM)	2004		90,30	23,00	7,80	23500	280.0
MAERSK BEATER	(IOM)	1997	4363	84,60	18,85	7,50	20020	237.0
MAERSK								
CHALLENGER	(IOM)	1986	2887	75,40	17,60	6,10	14400	192.0
(ex Oil Challenger-91, Challenger III-86, Sydfonn-86)								
MAERSK CUTTER	(GBR)	1983	1972	68,86	15,78	6,40	14400	182.0

MAERSK DEE (IOM)	2000	1863	56,64	14,60	6,01	6520	95.0
MAERSK DON (IOM)	2000	1863	56,64	14,60	6,00	6520	95.0
MAERSK HANDLER (IOM)	2002	2000	80,00	18,00	6,59	17500	198.0
MAERSK HELPER (IOM)	2002	2000	80,00	18,00	6,59	17500	198.0
MAERSK MARINER (GBR)	1986	3949	82,23	18,85	6,90	14900	170.0
MAERSK RETRIEVER (GBR)	1979	1894	67,14	15,85	6,46	13000	152.0
MAERSK RIDER (GBR)	1982	1894	67,14	15,85	6,46	14400	181.0
MAERSK ROVER (GBR)	1982	1894	67,14	15,85	6,46	14400	161.0
MAERSK SEARCHER (IOM)	1999	4140	82,00	18,85	7,50	18250	200.0
MAERSK SERVER (IOM)	2000	4013	82,00	18,85	7,50	18250	200.0
MAERSK SHIPPER (IOM)	1999	4013	82,00	18,85	7,58	18250	200.0
MAERSK SUPPORTER (IOM)	1999	4013	82,00	18,85	7,50	18250	214.0

Managed for Oxgate Security Co Ltd

MAERSK MAHONE (IOM)	1983	2322	71,76	16,51	6,25	10800	120.0

(ex Maersk Handler-02, Maersk Supporter-98, Mahone Bay-87)

Offshore services worldwide

Photographed from the stern, there is an excellent view of some of the equipment on the MAERSK SERVER.

(Jan Plug)

NOMIS SHIPPING LTD

183 Albert Quay, Aberdeen, AB11 5QA
Tel : 01224 210383   Fax : 01224 210582
E-mail : rory.deans@nomisshipping.com
Website : www.nomisshipping.com
Livery - Black or orange hull with white housing and bright yellow funnel

Name	Flag	Year						
ABERDONIAN	(GBR)	1977	480	44,75	10,82	4,95	3000	
DEA ARGOSY	(BHS)	1999	1402	61,00	13,80	4,90	5300	67.0
(ex Seacor Argosy-03)								
DEA CAPTAIN	(GBR)	1973	836	54,82	12,30	4,44	4000	43.0
(ex Power Express-95, Muhammed Ali-80, Smit-Lloyd 47-79)								
DEA CHALLENGER	(BHS)	1975	1217	58,85	12,02	4,81	6000	70.0
(ex Asia Maru-98, Aomjai 2-90, Selco Supply II-87, Ibis Six-80)								
DEA CHAMPION	(BHS)	1980	1235	60,36	14,00	5,01	6000	80.0
(ex Smit-Lloyd 71-98)								
DEA CHANCELLOR	(VCT)	1975	934	59,54	12,25	4,81	6160	72.0
(ex Chain Supplier-01, Bon Valor-98, Royal-86, Jason-80, Stella Salvator-77)								
DEA COMMANDER	(GBR)	1975	1152	58,98	12,02	4,12		
(ex Normand Gard-96, Normand Conger-85, Normand Vibran-81, Ocean Pilot-79, Normand Vibran-76)								
DEA CONQUEROR	(BHS)	1982	1236	60,49	14,00	5,25	6000	77.0
(ex Smit-Lloyd 73-98)								
DEA FIGHTER	(GBR)	1973	1022	53,17	11,74	3,80		
(ex Sea Sapphire-92, Ibis Two-81)								
DEA HUNTER	(GBR)	1979	1317	64,83	14,10	5,90	7342	113.0
(ex Triumph Sea-01, Acadian Mistral-01, Offshore Hunter-86, Kongsholm-84, Normand Hunter -84)								
DEA LINGUE	(VCT)	1973	786	54,81	12,30	4,97	4000	43.0
(ex Lingue-04, Smit-Lloyd 41-85)								
DEA MARINER	(GBR)	1975	846	53,22	11,03	3,46	4600	
(ex ODS Manta-93, Adil-86, Nor Truck-81)								
DEA ODYSSEY	(BHS)	1987	1256	58,04	13,50	5,06	5331	67.0
(ex Smit-Lloyd 57-04)								
DEA PILOT	(GBR)	1973	950	52,67	12,15	4,55	4020	
(ex Rossinant-94, Kentonvale Star-92, Bass Tide-87, Bass Shore-79)								
DEA PROTECTOR)	(GBR)	1974	1104	56,94	11,50	3,50	2000	n/a
(ex Scott Protector-04, Normand Carrier-89)								
DEA RANGER	(GBR)	1978/91	631	50,35	8,00	3,83	1800	n/a
(ex Normand Ondour-04, Balta Sound-91, Oddstein-86)								
DEA SAILOR	(BHS)	1981	516	42,50	8,86	3,36	1700	20.0
(ex Toisa Widgeon-04, Canmar Widgeon-90)								
DEA SCOUT	(BHS)	1981	516	42,50	8,86	3,36	1700	20.0
(ex Toisa Teal-04, Canmar Teal-90)								
DEA SEARCHER	(BHS)	1983	782	54,87	12,19	4,27	2250	30.0
(ex Toisa Petrel-03, Lynn Pelham-91)								
DEA SEEKER	(BHS)	1979	782	56,54	11,58	4,27	2250	30.0
(ex Toisa Puffin-04, Marsea One-91)								

DEA SERVER (BHS) 1979 863 56,54 11,58 3,70 2250 30.0
(ex Toisa Plover-03, Veesea-91, Kara Seal-91)
DEA SIGNAL (BRB) 1985 1558 65,03 14,50 6,36 9180 112.0
(ex Stirling Spica-02, Star Spica-96)
DEA SKIPPER (BHS) 1973 1292 63,89 13,31 5,84 10000 126.0
(ex Smit-Lloyd 105-97)
DEA SOUND (VCT) 1983 1521 67,59 14,05 5,97 9280 126.0
(ex Smit-Lloyd Sound-03, TS-52 Sound-93)
DEA SUPPLIER (IOM) 1975 1174 58,95 12,60 6,00 6160 70.0
(ex Normand Skipper-04)
DEA SUPPORTER (IOM) 1970 818 51,70 11,59 4,20 5750 n/a
(ex Mastodon-91)
DEA TRADER (GBR) 1979 1314 64,72 14,13 5,91 6000 95.0
(ex Emerald Sand-01, Terra Nova Sea-89, Acadian Tempest-87, Offshore Trader-86,
Normand Trader-84)
Also operate standby vessel

Viewed from the northern side of the harbour, the DEA RANGER leaves Aberdeen on 7 July 2004.

(David Dodds)

NORTH STAR SHIPPING (ABERDEEN) LTD
207 Albert Quay, Aberdeen, AB11 5FS
Tel : 01224 592206 Fax : 01224 212650
E-mail : north.star@craig-group.com
Website : www.craig-group.com
Livery - Dark orange or dark blue hull with buff housing; red/grey/black striped funnel.
GRAMPIAN (tbn) (GBR) 2005 48,25 11,00 1900
GRAMPIAN (tbn) (GBR) 2005 48,25 11,00 1900

GRAMPIAN (tbn)　(GBR)　2006　　48,25　11,00　　　　1900
GRAMPIAN (tbn)　(GBR)　2006　　48,25　11,00　　　　1900
GRAMPIAN
CHIEFTAIN　(GBR)　1976　424　39,30　9,68　3,80　1700　n/a
GRAMPIAN CITY　(GBR)　1976　425　39,30　9,68　3,80　1700　n/a
(ex Pindarus-84, Shielwood-77)
GRAMPIAN
CLANSMAN　(GBR)　1973　1165　58,95　12,62　4,65　2901　n/a
(ex O.D.R. 3-93, Ocean Fighter-88, Norindo Supplier-87, Norindo Star-80)
GRAMPIAN
CRUSADER　(GBR)　1976　1450　61,02　14,33　5,10　4201　n/a
(ex Hamilton Piper-92, Hamilton Piper 1-90, Hamilton Piper-87)
GRAMPIAN DEE　(GBR)　1975　419　39,30　9,48　3,79　1440　n/a
(ex Drot-90, Boston Halifax-86)
GRAMPIAN
DEFENDER　(GBR)　2002　800　47,10　11,10　5,80
(ex BUE Westray-04)
GRAMPIAN
EXPLORER　(GBR)　2003　2244　71,80　16,00　5,90　5460　n/a

The GRAMPIAN EXPLORER passes Gorleston on her way out of Great Yarmouth.

(Paul Gowen)

GRAMPIAN FALCON　(GBR) 1982　769　52,13　11,21　4,14　1300　n/a
(cx Burnhavon-90, Stirling Imp-87)
GRAMPIAN FAME　(GBR)　1975　1380　65,54　14,03　4,97　3200　n/a
(ex Red Sea Trader-92, Maersk Pacer-87)
GRAMPIAN
FRONTIER　(GBR)　1997　2065　69,90　14,50　6,51　8428　100.0

GRAMPIAN							
GUARDIAN (GBR)	1980	1112	57,70	12,20	3,80	2599	n/a

(ex Amazon Guardian-00, Grampian Guardian-00, Atlantic Guardian-97, Bigorange XV-91)

GRAMPIAN HAVEN (GBR) 1982 769 52,13 11,21 4,14 1300 n/a
(ex Portnahaven-90, Stirling Merlin-89)

GRAMPIAN
HIGHLANDER (GBR) 1975 1547 61,02 13,80 5,10 4201 n/a
(ex City of Aberdeen-90, Polar Fjord-90, Normand Providence-86, Stad Scandia-81)

GRAMPIAN
HUNTER (GBR) 1992 763 46,33 10,42 4,10 2134 n/a

GRAMPIAN
MONARCH (GBR) 1962 573 47,17 8,44 4,45 1500 n/a
(ex Myrevag-89, Myrefisk III-82)

GRAMPIAN
ORCADES (GBR) 1991 756 46,33 10,42 4,60 2134 n/a

GRAMPIAN
OSPREY (GBR) 1979 905 61,24 11,84 4,03 3200 n/a
(ex Sea Serv Osprey-96, Stirling Osprey-93)

GRAMPIAN OTTER (GBR) 1983 736 52,00 11,33 4,14 1300 n/a
(ex Johnshaven-90, Stirling Elf-88)

GRAMPIAN
PIONEER (GBR) 1981 501 42,25 10,00 4,30 1370 n/a
(ex Standby Pioneer-84)

GRAMPIAN PRIDE (GBR) 1981 501 42,25 10,04 4,56 1370 n/a
(ex Standby Pride-83)

GRAMPIAN PRINCE (GBR) 1984 1294 64,39 13,82 5,23 6000 n/a
(ex Al Mojil XXXV-96, Bellerophon-93, Agip Bellerophon-89)

GRAMPIAN
PROTECTOR (GBR) 1983 573 44,84 10,00 4,85 2134 n/a
(ex Standby Protector-86)

GRAMPIAN
RANGER (GBR) 2002 800 47,10 11,10 5,80
(ex BUE Stronsay-04)

GRAMPIAN SPRITE (GBR) 1982 766 52,13 11,21 4,14 1300 n/a
(ex Stirling Sprite-90)

GRAMPIAN STAR (GBR) 1988 560 45,42 9,22 5,41 1500 n/a
(ex North Safe-88, Rollanes-84)

GRAMPIAN
SUPPORTER (GBR) 1976 1369 65,54 14,03 4,98 3200 n/a
(ex Grampian Freedom-96, Maersk Puncher-91)

GRAMPIAN
SURVEYOR (GBR) 2003 2786 75,00 16,00 5,25 5982 n/a

GRAMPIAN
VENTURE (GBR) 1981 766 52,13 11,21 4,14 1300 n/a
(ex Sandhaven-90, Stirling Puck-87)

Offshore services in the North Sea

SBS MARINE LTD

Badentoy Road, Badentoy Industrial Park, Porthlethen, Aberdeen, AB12 4YA
Tel : 01224 784529   Fax : 01224 784528
E-mail : info@sbsl.com
Website : www.sbsl.com or www.sbsmarine.com
Livery - Black hull, white housing and red funnel with white band

SBS CIRRUS (GBR)	1985	2562	80,78	18,00	4,96	6120	n/a
(ex Active Duke-01)							
SBS NIMBUS (GBR)	2003	2500	73,40	16,60	6,50	5520	n/a
SBS STRATUS (GBR)	2003	2500	73,40	16,60	6,50	5520	n/a

Offshore supply services in the North Sea

It is evident that Aberdeen is an excellent location for ship photography. On this occasion, it is the SBS NIMBUS which is approaching the port on 7 September 2003.

(David Dodds)

SEAHORSE LTD

Mainport, Monahan Road, Cork, Ireland
Tel : +353 21 431 7900   Fax : +353 21 431 8381
E-mail : info@mainport.ie
Website : www.mainport.ie
Livery - Dark blue hull with white housing

Managed for Irish Mainport Ltd

PEARL (IRL)	1983	129665.36	13,09	4,60	6254	70.0
(ex Veesea Pearl-00, Droit de Parole-94, Cariboo-93, Fort Reliance-89)							
SEAHORSE							
SUPPORTER (IRL)	1974	692	52,68	11,66	4,05	2900	n/a
(ex Wendentor-91)							

Offshore services off the south-east coast of Ireland

SEALION SHIPPING LTD

Sealion House, The Courtyard, 17 West Street, Farnham, GU9 7DR
Tel : 01252 737773   Fax : 01252 737770
E-mail : iperrott@sealionshipping.co.uk
Website : www.sealionshipping.co.uk
Livery - Orange hull with buff housing and wheelhouse; buff funnel with company badge

TOISA							
CONQUEROR (GBR)	2001	2401	73,80	16,05	6,28	5228	n/a
TOISA CORAL (GBR)	1999	2401	73,80	16,05	6,33	5228	n/a
TOISA CREST (GBR)	1999	2401	73,80	16,05	6,29	5228	n/a
TOISA DARING	2006		69,00	16,60	6,20	12236	160.0
TOISA DAUNTLESS	2006		69,00	16,60	6,20	12236	160.0
TOISA DEFIANT	2006		69,00	16,60	6,20	12236	160.0
TOISA							
INDEPENDENT (GBR)	2003	3100	83,20	19,00	5,92	7341	n/a
TOISA INTREPID (BHS)	1998	2990	82,85	19,05	6,34	6600	n/a
TOISA INVINCIBLE (BHS)	1998	2990	82,85	19,05	6,32	6600	n/a
TOISA LEOPARD (GBR)	1983	846	61,73	11,84	4,00	3520	n/a
(ex TNT Leopard-90)							
TOISA LION (BHS)	1983	846	61,73	11,84	4,03	3520	n/a
(ex TNT Lion-90)							
TOISA MARINER (BHS)	1980	2113	72,07	16,01	5,27	5480	n/a
(ex Marinous-90, Sable Sea-89, Balder Baffin-87)							
TOISA TIGER (BHS)	1983	846	61,73	11,84	4,00	3520	n/a
(ex TNT Tiger-90)							
TOISA VALIANT (BHS)	2005	3484	80,50	18,00	6,10	6434	
TOISA VIGILANT (BHS)	2005	3484	80,50	18,00	6,10	6434	
TOISA VOYAGER (BHS)	2005	3484	80,50	18,00	6,10	6434	

Offshore services worldwide

SPECIALIST MARINE SERVICES LTD

Ocean House, Waterside Business Park, Livingstone Road, Hessle, HU13 0EG
Tel : 01482 648283   Fax : 01482 648284
E-mail : sms@specialist-marine.co.uk
Website : www.specialist-marine.com
Livery - Red hull with white housing; red funnel
        Black hull with white housing; black funnel (Chermonorneftegaz vessel)

GUARDSMAN (BHS)	1977	1687	65,87	14,05	5,83	4200	n/a
(ex Smit Manta-98, Smit-Lloyd 62-86)							
STATESMAN (GBR)	1976	1976	78,00	14,03	6,12	9460	132.0
(ex Sun Wrestler-99, Baru-91, Schnoorturm-87)							

Managed for Chermonorneftegaz Tech Fleet (Ukraine)

ATREK (UKR)	1983	1491	67,70	13,97	4,70	8347	103.0

Offshore services worldwide

TRICO SUPPLY (UK) LTD

14 Albyn Terrace, Aberdeen, AB10 1YP
Tel : 01224 633366   Fax : 01224 630818
Website : www.tricomarine.com
Livery - Dark red hull with cream housing and funnel

Managed for Trico Supply AS

NORTHERN CANYON (GBR)	2002	3707	84,00	18,80		7950	n/a
NORTHERN CHASER (GBR) (ex Andrew Viking-97)	1991	2335	73,60	16,40	6,00	15612	166.0
NORTHERN MARINER (GBR) (ex Suffolk Mariner-97)	1986	1532	60,20	14,81	5,71	4779	n/a
NORTHERN QUEEN (GBR) (ex Mona Viking-97, Sea Guardian-90, Sea Worker-84)	1982	1833	67,42	17,23	6,08	6960	n/a
NORTHERN SUPPORTER (GBR) (ex Suffolk Supporter-97)	1996	1969	67,00	16,00	5,92	5452	n/a

Offshore services in the North Sea

The TOISA INTREPID near Aberdeen on 19 February 2004.

(David Dodds)

TUGS - UK

ADSTEAM (UK) LIMITED

11 Marina Court, Castle Street, Hull, HU1 1TX
Tel : 01482 337650   Fax : 01482 337683
Website : www.adsteam.com.au
Livery - Black hull with white housing; buff funnel bearing "A" logo

Based on the River Mersey and Barrow

ADSTEAM MERCIA	1990	449	32,50	10,00	3,30	3860	42.6
(ex Sun Mercia-05)							
BRAMLEY MOORE	1984	336	33,00	9,96	4,60	3440	38.0
CANADA	1980	282	30,21	9,45	4,40	2640	32.0
GLADSTONE	1977	256	30,00	8,82	3,03	2400	30.0
(ex TS Herkules-94, Herkules-90)							
TRAFALGAR	1998	369	29,31	11,88	3,40	5600	63.0
WATERLOO	1987	298	31,15	9,76	3,40	3440	36.0

Based in the Falkland Islands

INDOMITABLE	1979	416	35,74	9,26	4,22	3520	55.0

Based at Felixstowe and Harwich

BENTLEY	1996	381	32,72	11,96	4,25	4825	61.0
BRIGHTWELL	1986	256	28,80	9,05	4,06	3400	40.0
MELTON	1996	381	32,72	11,96	3,80	4825	61.0
TRIMLEY	1991	371	30,64	10,24	4,11	3860	43.0

The busy container berths at Felixstowe ensure plenty of work for the port's tugs. The BENTLEY assists a container ship on 1 September 2002.

(David Dixon)

Based on the Humber

ADSTEAM FERRIBY	2005	243	24,55	11,49	5,40	5592	70.4
ADSTEAM KEELBY	1986	480	33,92	10,82	5,15	4800	61.0
(ex Redcliffe-05, W J Trotter)							
COLLINGWOOD	1981	281	30,64	9,33	2,66	2640	32.0
LADY ALMA	1996	379	29,11	11,88	3,40	5600	59.0
LADY ANYA	1990	364	30,58	11,50	3,40	4800	53.0
LADY CONSTANCE	1982	285	30,21	9,73	2,81	2640	32.0
LADY DEBBIE	1978	369	35,01	11,55	4,54	2920	50.0
LADY ELIZABETH	1981	285	30,21	9,73	2,81	2640	32.0
LADY JOSEPHINE	1991	364	30,58	11,50	3,40	4800	53.0
LADY KATHLEEN	1991	364	30,58	11,50	3,40	4800	53.0
LADY LAURA	2001	353	30,60	11,20	4,05	4800	70.0
LADY MOIRA	1998	267	29,70	9,60	3,75	4800	50.0
(ex Peng-99, Peng Chau-99)							
LADY STEPHANIE	1984	285	30,21	9,73	4,61	2640	32.0
LADY SUSAN	1984	285	30,21	9,73	4,61	2640	32.0

The LADY SUSAN is being overhauled on the slipway at Grimsby on 28 June 2004.

(David Dixon)

Based on River Medway

ADSTEAM HARTY	2006	243	24,55	11,49	5,40	5592	70.4
ADSTEAM WARDEN	2006	243	24,55	11,49	5,40	5592	70.4
ADSTEAM VICTORY	2000	495	33,00	11,50	5,30	4894	64.8
(ex Gurroung-05)							
LADY BRENDA	1985	298	38,00	10,27	3,15	3200	45.0
(ex Kenley-91, launched as Yokosuka Maru No. 2)							

The LADY EMMA H hurries up the River Medway on 19 June 2005.

(Bernard McCall))

LADY EMMA H	1998	267	29,70	9,60	3,75	3600	49.7
(ex Lady Emma-98, Chek Chau-98)							
LADY MARIA	1975	225	29,00	9,96	4,02	2440	40.0
(ex Yarra-00, Buccaneer-97)							
LADY MORAG	1983	365	36,28	10,52	3,15	3400	50.0
(ex Kestrel-91, Kuroshio-91)							
Based on River Thames							
COBHAM	1984	287	30,10	9,22	3,23	2800	29.3
(ex Dextrous-00)							
LADY CECILIA	1991	364	30,58	11,50	3,40	4800	53.6
LADY SARAH	1991	364	30,58	11,50	3,40	4800	53.0
SHORNE	1984	287	30,10	9,22	3,23	2800	30.8
(ex Deft-00)							
SUN ANGLIA	1985	336	33,00	9,50	4,72	3440	39.7
SUN SURREY	1992	399	30,10	10,50	4,67	3860	43.0
SUN SUSSEX	1992	378	30,10	10,50	4,67	3860	40.5
SUN THAMES	1982	287	33,10	9,96	4,52	2640	25.3
Based at Southampton							
DEBEN	1990	371	30,64	10,24	4,11	3860	43.0
HAMTUN	1985	250	29,37	9,12	4,58	2750	35.0
LADY MADELEINE	1996	381	32,72	11,96	3,80	4825	61.0
LYNDHURST	1996	379	30,00	11,60	3,80	4200	43.0

REDBRIDGE	1995	399	33,00	11,73	4,86	4104	45.0
SIR BEVOIS	1985	250	29,37	9,12	4,58	2750	35.0

Coastal and harbour towage at various ports around the UK

Part of the Adsteam Group
As we go to press, we understand that most if not all tugs are to be renamed with an ADSTEAM prefix.

ASSOCIATED BRITISH PORTS HOLDINGS PLC
150 Holborn, London, EC1N 2LR
Tel : 020 74301177   Fax : 020 74301384
E-mail : pr@abports.co.uk
Website : www.abports.co.uk
Livery - Various

FURNESS ABBEY	1997	120	19,65	6,04	1,87	720	10.6
HUMBER SENTINEL	1991	235	28,25	9,69	2,50	1080	

A W MARINE SERVICES LTD
11 Ewan Close, Leigh-on-Sea, Essex
Tel : 01702 557156

HORTON	1968	31	17,10	4,70	2,00	243	6.2

Contrasting tug designs are evident in this view of the OLIVER FELIX at Southampton berthed alongside a former US Army tug on 5 June 2004.

(Bob Allen)

G BAKER MARINE LTD

Operational base : Berth 50, Dock Gate 4, Atlantic Way, Southampton, SO14 3QN
Contact address : 37 Andes Close, Ocean Village, Southampton
Tel/Fax : 023 8033 7889

CHIEFTON	1930	72				720	
(ex Chief-04, Filip)							
DEBORAH	1958	35				143	
(ex M.S.C. Deborah-88)							
DIDO	1958	35				140	
(ex M.S.C. Dido-88)							
JOAN	1972	90	17,65	5,25	2,79	330	
NORAH	1973	90	17,65	5,25	2,79	330	
OLIVER FELIX *	1962	160	28,66	7,95	3,26	1080	14.5
(ex Polgarth-90)							
SUSAN	1968	80	21,50	6,40	2,90	600	6.0
(ex Wyepress, Felicity-98)							

Towage on the south coast of England
* Honduras flag

BARTLETT CREEK SHIPPING LTD

139 Watling Street, Gillingham, Kent, ME7 2YY
Tel : 01634 234147

NIPASHORE	1983	18	13,20	4,00	1,75	180	1.5

Towage services on the River Thames and River Medway

*The Barrow-registered **Avanti C** is seen undertaking plough dredging duties near Cardiff Barrage on 3 March 2005.*

(Bob Allen)

BAY TOWAGE & SALVAGE CO LTD

Dock Office, Anchorline Basin, Barrow-in-Furness, Cumbria, LA14 2TB
Tel : 01229 830388   Fax : 01229 871011
E-mail : info@baytowage.co.uk
Website : www.baytowage.co.uk
Livery - Black hull, white wheelhouse with dayglow orange band on top

ALBICORE	1990	110	20,00	6,70	2,40	760	8.0
(ex Sarah D-01)							
AVANTI C	1978	33	15,25	4,75	1,80	480	5.0
KAMSAR	1982	40	15,70	4,80	2,20	730	7.5
TIOGA B	1981	38	15,93	5,03	2,00	730	11.0
(ex Anglian Maid-95, Gray Delta-91)							

Towage services at Barrow-in-Furness and on the River Mersey; marine services and dredging support on the west coast of the UK

ALAN C BENNETT & SONS LTD

Lingley House, Commissioners Road, Strood, Rochester, Kent, ME2 4EE
Tel : 01634 290780   Fax : 01634 290891
Livery : Black with white trim, white housing and blue funnel, black top separated by white band; Foster Yeoman funnels bear a white letter "Y"

ARGONAUT	1963	115	24,50	6,60	3,45	875	13.0
Managers for Foster Yeoman Ltd							
SEA CHALLENGE II	1969	70	20,36	6,70	2,94	1060	13.0
(ex Eduard-00, Jumbo-83, Argus 5)							
STEVEN B	1971		25,24	5,50	2,50	1200	15.0
(ex Bever-00)							

Towage and lighterage services on the River Thames
A wholly-owned subsidiary of Foster Yeoman Ltd

With Canary Wharf in the background, the SEA CHALLENGE II was photographed on 13 July 2002, the day of a barge race on the upper Thames.

(Alan Rose)

BLYTH HARBOUR COMMISSION

79 Bridge Street, Blyth, Northumberland, NE24 2AW
Tel : 01670 352066   Fax : 01670 355169
Website : www.portofblyth.co.uk
Livery - Light blue hull and white wheelhouse with orange trim

BLYTH ENDEAVOUR	1991	43	16,89	5,29	2,10	600	6.0

Bed levelling, also coastal and harbour towage on east coast of England

BOATWERK (THAMES) LTD

British Gypsum Jetty, Church Manorway, Erith, Kent, DA8 1BQ
Tel : 01322 438305

KATHY M	1997	14,00	4,50	1,80	450	4.1
MONARCH M	2000	9,80	3,00	1,40	180	1.2

Towage and marine services on the River Thames

PORT OF BOSTON LTD

Dock Office, The Docks, Boston, Lincolnshire, PE21 6BN
Tel : 01205 365571   Fax : 01205 310126
E-mail : administrator@portofboston.co.uk
Website : www.portofboston.co.uk
Livery - Black hull, white housing and wheelhouse; buff funnel

BOSTONIAN	1967	50	21,30	6,10	2,00	528	7.0

Towage service at port of Boston

The BOSTONIAN is seen in the River Haven on 2 October 2004.

(David Dixon)

BOSTON PUTFORD OFFSHORE SAFETY LTD
Columbus Buildings, Waveney Road, Lowestoft, Suffolk, NR32 1BS
Tel : 01502 573366   Fax : 01502 581500
Website : www.seacormarine.com

PLANTER	1967	38	16,76	4,57	2,46	420	5.0
(ex Batty, Planter)							

BRIGGS MARINE CONTRACTORS LTD
West Dock, Burntisland, Fife, KY3 9AU
Tel : 01592 872939   Fax : 01592 873975
E-mail : bmc@briggsmarine.com
Website : www.briggsmarine.com
Livery - Black hull with buff housing and funnel, white wheelhouse

FORTH BOXER	1995	83	18,60	6,06	1,65	440	6.0
FORTH CONSTRUCTOR	1967/94	265	28,50	9,45	2,90	1240	17.5
(ex Broodbank-95)							
FORTH DRUMMER	1967	114	25,30	7,35	2,87	1240	16.0
(ex Lady Laura-00)							
FORTH ENGINEER	1996	102	18,70	8,06	1,80	600	7.7
FORTH FIGHTER	1985/2001	55	23,50	7,50	1,50	640	8.0
(ex Gemsar-01)							
FORTH INSPECTOR		722	18,70	8,06	1,76	601	7.8
(ex DMS Eagle-03)							
JOSINE	1974		13,00	3,40	2,00	240	
SYLVESTER	1974		14,00	6,00	0,90	320	

Coastal towage and marine civil engineering

The FORTH BOXER approaches Peterhead on 7 September 2002.

(David Dodds)

BRISTOL INDUSTRIAL MUSEUM
Princes Wharf, Wapping Road, Bristol
Tel : 0117 925 1470

JOHN KING	1935	49	19,81	5,18	2,16	300	
(ex Durdham-92, Pride-86, Peter Leigh-78)							
MAYFLOWER	1861	32	19,29	3,65	2,19	150	

Both preserved in the City Docks, Bristol

BRITISH WATERWAYS BOARD
Harbour House, West Quay, The Dock, Gloucester, GL1 2LG
Tel : 01452 318020   Fax : 01452 318706
E-mail : enquiries.southwest@britishwaterways.co.uk
Website : www.britishwaterways.co.uk
Livery - Black hull with blue housing and wheelhouse

SPEEDWELL	1967	50	17,07	4,88	2,44	330	2.5

Marine services on the Gloucester & Sharpness Canal

JAMES BUTCHER & SONS LTD
14 Broad Street, Portsmouth, Hants, PO1 2JE
Tel : 023 9282 2584   Fax : 023 9287 4666
E-mail : tug@blueboattrips.com
Livery - Sky blue hull with white wheelhouse and company emblem

CAROL JAMES	1983		15,30	4,60	2,20	527	5.0
GARY JAMES			14,45	4,40	2,00		5.0
GUY JAMES	1995	57	16,90	5,29	2,10	940	13.5
JACK JAMES	2002		16,90	5,29	2,30	1080	14.5
JANET JAMES	1983		14,20	4,20	2,00	480	3.8

Towage services at Portsmouth; also operate pleasure boats

The NEW ROSS 1
is seen off Penarth
marina.

(Richard Page)

CARDIFF COMMERCIAL BOAT OPERATORS LTD
27 Syr Davids Avenue, Cardiff, CF5 1GH
Tel : 02920 236366
Livery - Black hull with white wheelhouse

NEW ROSS 1	1986		14,40	4,20	2,05	349	6.0

Towage and marine services in South Wales

CARMET TUG COMPANY LTD
44 Private Drive, Barnston, Wirral, Merseyside, L61 1DE
Tel : 0151 327 8018   Fax : 0151 328 1212
E-mail : tugs@carmet.co.uk
Website : www.carmet.co.uk
Livery - Black hull with white wheelhouse and cream housing

AUDREY	1961	38	18,74	5,18	2,29	495	6.5
(ex Brenda)							
M.S.C. VICEROY	1975	137	28,38	7,31	3,44	1280	14.0
M.S.C. VICTORY	1974	137	28,38	7,31	3,44	1280	14.0
M.S.C. VIKING	1976	137	28,38	7,31	3,44	1280	14.0
M.S.C. VOLANT	1976	137	28,38	7,31	3,44	1280	14.0
VIGOUR	1966	33	15,40	5,50	1,90	375	
(ex Pushdale H, Baas)							

Coastal towage and towage services on the Manchester Ship Canal

Stanlow Oil Dock is the setting for this view of the M.S.C. VICTORY on 8 September 2001. Only the eastern side of the dock is now used by tankers.

(Roy Cressey)

CATTEWATER HARBOUR COMMISSIONERS
2 The Barbican, Plymouth, Devon, PL1 2LR
Tel : 01752 66934
Website : www.plymouthport.org
Livery - Blue hull with white wheelhouse

PRINCE ROCK	2003	100	18,87	6,56	3,04	1000	15.0

Towage services at Plymouth

CLEANAWAY LTD
Rainham Lighterage, Ferry Lane, Rainham, Essex, RM13 9DA
Tel : 01708 632200   Fax : 01708 524612
Livery - Black hull, brown housing with company logo and white housing

JIM HIGGS	1959	109	25,73	6,76	3,04	1000	15.0

(ex Lord Ritchie-85)

Lighterage work on the River Thames

CLYDE MARINE SERVICES LTD
Victoria Harbour, Greenock, PA15 1HW
Tel : 01475 721281   Fax : 01475 888023
E-mail : enquiries@clyde-marine.co.uk
Website : www.clyde-marine.co.uk

BATTLER	2004	110	19,65	6,04	2,70	1440	20.8
BEAVER BAY	1977	42	16,00	4,80	1,80	380	5.0
(ex Loch Shiel)							
BITER	1982	42	16,00	4,80	1,30	796	11.0
(ex Haki-01, Salud-82)							
BOOJUMBAY	1964	30	15,00	4,40	1,70	365	5.0
(ex Medway-91, Niger-64)							
FENCER	1976	17	11,00	4,00	1,20	127	1.5

Marine services on the River Clyde

The BEAVER BAY was photographed making good headway in the Clyde on 24 July 2004.
(Dominic McCall)

COASTAL LAUNCH SERVICES

The Saeter, East Boldre, Nr. Brockenhurst, Hampshire, SO42 7WU
Tel : 01590 626247   Fax : 01590 626301
E-mail : coastal@btconnect.com
Website : www.coastallaunchservicesltd.co.uk

JESSICA S	1983	126	20,02	9,15	1,50	800	9.5
(ex S.B.1 -92)							
SARAH GREY	1999	107	25,00	9,60	1,85	1400	18.0

Marine civil engineering and dredging support

COASTLINE SURVEYS LTD

Unit 17/18, Frampton-on-Severn Industrial Estate, Bridge Road, Frampton-on-Severn, GL10 7HE
Tel : 01452 740941   Fax : 01452 740811
E-mail : info@coastlinesurveys.co.uk
Website : www.coastlinesurveys.co.uk
Livery - Dark blue hull, white housing; blue funnel

FLAT HOLM	1976	129	24,00	7,42	2,89	700	10.0
(ex UKD Flat Holm-99, Flat Holm-97, Al Khubar 3 -86)							

Marine civil engineering and survey services

COASTWORKS LTD

8 Allanton Park Terrace, Fairlie, Ayrshire, KA29 0AW
Tel : 01475 568572   Fax : 01475 568153
E-mail : info@coastworks.co.uk
Website : www.coastworks.co.uk

REGIS II	1977	10,60	3,60	1,10	160	1.5

Marine services on the west coast of Scotland

COLERAINE HARBOUR COMMISSIONERS

4 Riversdale Road, Coleraine, BT52 1RY
Tel : 028 7034 2012   Fax : 028 7035 2000
E-mail : info@coleraineharbour.f9.co.uk

CONFIDENCE	1983	38	16,80	5,20	2,50	720	11.0
(ex Plym Echo-04, Gray Echo-96)							

Towage services at Coleraine

CORY ENVIRONMENTAL LTD

2 Coldbath Square, London EC1R 5HL
Tel : 020 885 35434   Fax : 020 885 88388
E-mail : info@coryenvironmental.co.uk
Website : www.coryenvironmental.co.uk
Livery - Black with white housing and black/white/black funnel with company logo

GENERAL VIII	1965	77	25,69	6,40	3,14	1196	11.0
MERIT	1964	83	25,30	6,09	2,74	1196	11.0
(ex Lingo)							
MERSINA	1955	79	24,38	5,97	2,92	750	10.0
(ex Repulse)							
RECRUIT	1952	91	24,38	5,97	2,93	1196	11.0
REGAIN	1998	126	25,90	9,40	2,10	1610	17.5
RESOLVE	1994	49	15,24	4,87	1,10	250	3.0
RETAINER	1979	120	23,55	6,60	2,50	2096	13.4
(ex Oil Retainer-90)							

Lighterage services on the River Thames

Modellers appreciate overhead views of vessels in order to see precise details of deck fittings. The GENERAL VIII heads up the Thames on 28 April 2005.

(Alan Small)

On the same date, the RETAINER passes the same location, Tilbury Cruise Terminal.

(Alan Small)

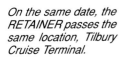

CPBS MARINE SERVICES

115 St Josephs Vale, London SE3 0XQ
Tel : 0800 0191516   Fax : 020 8297 5077
E-mail : info@cpbs.co.uk
Website : www.cpbsmarineservices.co.uk

BULLDOG	35	11,76	3,86	1,30	280	
GUNDOG		14,50	6,06	1,20	250	2.0

Towage and marine services on the River Thames

Late news: The above two tugs have been sold and replaced by

WATCHDOG		11,00	3,30	1,10

The BULLDOG awaits her next duty on the Thames on 29 April 2003.

(John Southwood)

L & J F CUNNINGHAM

90 Greencastle Pier Road, Kilkeel, Newry, County Down, BT34 4LR
Livery - Black hull, brown housing and white wheelhouse with buff funnel

MOURNE SHORE	1964	101	22,99	7,45	2,59	800	14.0
(ex Bugsier 29-93)							
MOURNE VALLEY	1961	57	18,6	5,30	2,70	495	7.0
(ex Afon Cefni-89)							

Towage services in the Carlingford Lough area

DEANS TUGS & WORKBOATS LTD

10 Wentworth Way, Craven Street, Hull, HU9 2AX
Tel : 01482 219277   Fax : 0860 301116
Livery - Black and blue hull, blue housing and white wheelhouse with blue funnel and white stripe

ANGLIAN	1964	98	24,45	7,34	3,30	1050	13.0
(ex Tugman-83)							
FELIX TOW	1955	28	15,00	4,20	2,50	250	2.5
(ex Felix-Tow)							
FREIGHT ENDEAVOUR	1967	38	18,00	4,88	2,50	420	3.0
(ex Placer-74)							
GILLIAN KNIGHT	1963	32	18,75	4,88	2,13	250	2.0
LASHETTE	1971	156	24,00	8,50	2,60	720	10.0
LINFORD	1966	122	26,70	7,80	4,00	1600	16.0
(ex Plankton-91)							
MARY	1973	50	18,28	5,26	2,59	330	3.3
ORSETT	1966	122	26,70	7,80	4,00	1600	16.0
(ex Placard-91)							
PRIMROSE	1906	53	22,6	4,90	2,70	360	5.4
SHOVETTE	1974	156	24,00	8,50	2,60	720	10.0
(ex Grey Lash-83)							

Towage services at Hull and the River Humber

John Dean has tugs of various designs and vintage in his fleet. Berthed astern of the GILLIAN KNIGHT is the FREIGHT ENDEAVOUR, a pusher tug built for use on the inland waterways of the UK. The tugs are seen at Hull on 12 December 2003.

(Roy Cressey)

The LASHETTE is one of two sisterships in the Dean fleet. She was photographed as she towed a barge out of Immingham on 15 March 2003.

(David Dixon)

DELTA MARINE

5 Gladstone Terrace, Lerwick, Shetland, ZE1 0EG
Tel : 01595 694799   Fax : 01595 692685
Website : www.delta-marine.co.uk
Livery - Blue hull with white housing and company emblem

VOE SERVICE	1989	55	18,42	6,00	1,70	480	7.5
VOE TRADER	1997	199	25,85	9,55	2,00	1600	19.0
VOE VENTURE	1994	121	18,42	8,04	2,00	900	14.0
VOE VIKING	2005		26,00	11,50	2,25	2400	32.0

Towage and civil engineering services around Europe

A placid winter scene at Scalloway as the VOE VENTURE rests at the quayside on Christmas Day, 2004.

(Dominic McCall)

DOVER HARBOUR BOARD

Harbour House, Marine Parade, Dover, Kent, CT17 9BU
Tel : 01304 240400   Fax : 01304 240465
E-mail : pr@doverport.co.uk
Website : www.doverport.co.uk
Livery - Dark blue hull with white housing and blue funnel

DHB DAUNTLESS	2000	304	30,82	10,20	4,08	4820	55.0
DHB DOUGHTY	2000	304	30,82	10,20	4,08	4820	55.0

Towage services at the port of Dover

THE DUNKIRK LITTLE SHIP RESTORATION TRUST

c/o Cottage by the Lake, Hook Shore, Warsash, SO31 9HF
E-mail : jerrylewis@care4free.net
Website : www.adis.org.uk

CHALLENGE	1931	238	30,47	8,01	1,98	1100

Preserved steam tug seen at various ports on the south coast of England

ENVIRONMENT AGENCY
Kings Meadow House, Kings Meadow Road, Reading, Berkshire, RG1 8DQ
E-mail : enquiries@environment-agency.gov.uk
Website : www.environment-agency.gov.uk
Livery - Black hull, green housing and white wheelhouse with buff funnel

FALCONBROOK	1958	22	13,72	4,18	1,70	260	
(ex Caspar C-02, General V-84, Blackboys-76)							
VER	1956	14	13,41	3,20	1,37	178	1.5
(ex Brent Lee)							

The FALCONBROOK was photographed during a barge race on the River Thames in July 2002.
(Alan Rose)

MICHAEL F EWINGS (SHIPPING) LTD
15 - 19 Corporation Square, Belfast, BT1 3AJ
Tel : 02890 90 242242   Fax : 02890 90 235776
E-mail : info@mfewings.com

MICHAEL FRANCIS	2000	16,89	5,29	2,24	940	12.5

Towage services at Belfast

FALMOUTH TOWAGE COMPANY LTD
The Docks, Falmouth, Cornwall, TR11 4NR
Tel : 01326 319451   Fax : 01326 319451
Website : www.ap-group.com
Livery - Orange hull with white housing; black funnel with white band

| ST PIRAN | 1960 | 316 | 39,07 | 9,05 | 3,70 | 1350 | 22.0 |
| (ex Dalegarth-84) | | | | | | | |

A&P Falmouth Ltd

ANKORVA	1967	167	28,22	8,03	2,43	1580	20.0
(ex Komet-01, Comet-93)							
PERCUIL	1967	167	28,22	8,03	2,43	1580	20.0
(ex Kiklop-01, Cyclop-93)							

Coastal and harbour towage at Falmouth

The ANKORVA assists the Royal Fleet Auxiliary vessel ARGUS at Falmouth in April 2005.
(Chris Jones)

FELIXARC MARINE LTD

North Quay, The Dock, Felixstowe, IP11 8SY
Tel : 01394 676497   Fax : 01394 674039
Website : www.felixarcmarine.co.uk
Livery - Black hull with white housing; black funnel with yellow band

GRAY JUMBO	1986	97	18,42	8,04	1,50	740	12.0
GRAY MAMMOTH	1989	224	27,05	10,00	2,06	804	14.0
GRAY SALVOR	1991	40	16,50	5,20	2,58	850	11.0
GRAY TEST	1996	55	19,50	6,04	2,20	1342	17.5
(ex Anglian Man-00)							
GRAY VIXEN	1991	40	16,50	5,20	2,58	850	11.0
SUN LONDON	1977	275	32,92	9,61	4,17	2640	45.0

Coastal towage and marine civil engineering; harbour towage at Great Yarmouth and Felixstowe.

Part of Adsteam Group

The GRAY VIXEN provides assistance to the EIDE BARGE 33 within the narrow confines of the harbour at Great Yarmouth.

(Paul Gowen)

FENLAND DISTRICT COUNCIL
Harbour Master's Office, West Bank, Sutton Bridge, Lincolnshire, PE12 9QR
Tel : 01406 351530   Fax : 01406 351350
Livery - Black with white wheelhouse

FENLANDER	1999	35	14,44	4,73	2,05	600	7.6

Towage and pilot launch services at Sutton Bridge

DAVID FERRAN & SONS LTD
Hurst House, 2nd Floor, 15/19 Corporation Square, Belfast, BT1 3AJ
Tel : 028 9032 5751   Fax : 028 9043 8470
E-mail : justin@davidferran.co.uk
Website : www.davidferran.co.uk
Livery - Dark blue hull, white housing

DAVID ANDREWS	1971	54	18,60	5,80	2,50	525	6.5
EILEEN	1975		9,14	4,17	2,00	127	2.0
FARSET OF BELFAST	2003		15,40	5,20	1,80	1100	14.6
SALLY	1975		9,14	4,17	2,00	127	2.0
VERA LOCKHART	1974		10,97	4,27	2,00	250	3.5

Harbour towage and line-handling in Belfast

FORTH PORTS PLC

Tower Place, Leith, Edinburgh, EH1 7DB
Tel : 0131 5558700   Fax : 0131 5537462
E-mail : drew.simpson@forthports.co.uk
Website : www.forthports.co.uk
Livery - Black hull with cream housing; blue funnel with company badge

BEAMER	1983	251	29,42	8,60	4,00	1800	20.0
FIDRA	1995	363	30,00	11,50	5,30	5400	50.0
OXCAR	1978	250	30,64	9,00	4,55	2660	30.0
SEAL CARR	1983	251	29,42	8,60	4,00	1800	20.0

Harbour towage at Leith and on the Firth of Forth

FOWEY HARBOUR COMMISSIONERS

Harbour Office, Albert Quay, Fowey, Cornwall, PL23 1AJ
Tel : 01726 832740   Fax : 01726 833738
E-mail : fhc@foweyharbour.co.uk
Website : www.foweyharbour.co.uk
Livery - Black and green hull with yellow trim, buff and cream housing and wheelhouse

PENDENNICK	1964	132	27,97	7,85	3,13	970	14.5
(ex Dunelm-88)							
PENLEATH	1986		12,70	4,20	1,66	360	3.0
POLMEAR	2004		14,65	5,50	1,65	440	10.0
TREGEAGLE	1964	131	28,20	7,19	3,36	1000	15.0
(ex Forth-86, Flying Demon-84)							

Harbour towage and marine services at Fowey and Par

The TREGEAGLE passes Bodinnick on a fine spring evening in 2003.

(Bernard McCall)

GARELOCH SUPPORT SERVICES (PLANT) LTD

Rhu Marina, Rhu, Argyll & Bute, G84 8LH
Tel : 01436 821277   Fax : 01436 821288
E-mail : angus@gssplant.freeserve.co.uk
Website : www.gssplant.co.uk
Livery - Black hull, white housing; dark blue funnel

JULIA M	1975		10,00	5,00	1,80	180	3.0
LAURA M	2002	68	20,20	8,25	1,85	525	12.0
LESLEY M	1993	135	20,00	9,00	1,50	760	8.0
(ex MCS Menno-04, Sabrina-96)							
MARY M	1999	44	15,00	7,00	1,50	504	4.5

Marine civil engineering around the UK

GENERAL MARINE LTD

30 Ferry St, Isle of Dogs, London E14 3DT
Tel : 020 7791 2895   Fax : 020 7791 2875
Livery - Black hull, red housing and white wheelhouse; white funnel with red diamond

LORD DEVONPORT	1959	109	25,73	6,76	3,04	935	
REGARDER	1958	69	22,43	5,70	2,71	500	6.0
(ex Regard-91)							
REVENGE	1948	61	19,80	5,20	2,40	500	7.0
SIR AUBREY	1962		22,25	5,18	2,89	650	9.0
SUNCREST	1961	144	28,58	7,45	3,37	1340	13.0
(ex Sunwind-85, Sun XXIII-84)							
WAVERLEY	1960	109	25,73	6,76	3,04	935	
(ex Lord Waverley)							

Towage services on the River Thames

G. P. S. MARINE CONTRACTORS LTD

Lockside House, Chatham Docks, Kent, ME4 4SW
Tel : 01634 401444   Fax : 01634 843456
Livery - Black hull with brown housing and white wheelhouse; black funnel with white band
bearing the letters GPS

ALEXANDRA	1963	164	30,64	8,08	3,70	1050	18.0
FRISTON DOWN	1964	99	24,97	6,20	3,30	1250	21.0
MURIA	1960	128	29,21	6,94	3,00	900	9.0
(ex Independent II-00)							
NAPIA	1965	128	29,21	6,94	3,00	900	9.0
(ex Volharding 12-00)							
RACIA	1964	78	24,80	6,02	2,90	600	9.0
(ex Condor IX-02, Condor-00, Pieter Goedkoop-82)							
RICHARD HART	1949	75	19,84	4,06	2,25	365	5.3
(ex William George-75)							

Towage services on the River Thames, River Medway, and coastal towage

The SIR AUBREY at Tilbury Dock on 5 June 2004.

(Ian Willett, courtesy PLA)

On 7 February 2004, the two tugs in the fleet of Griffin Towage, KINGSTON and newly-acquired CHIEF, were photographed at Spencers Quay, Cowes. The CHIEF was later renamed CHIEFTON and has since been sold on to G Baker Marine Ltd.

(Brian Ralfs)

GRIFFIN TOWAGE / J A EVELEGH
Pleystowe Farmhouse, Rusper Road, Capel, Dorking, RH5 5HE
Tel : 07956 351933   Fax : 01305 826056

KINGSTON	1962	113	26,90	6,90	3,00	720	23.0
(ex Sun XXIV-92)							
PRINCETON	1965	148	28,70	7,00	3,90	1350	20.0
(ex Kapitan Engler-05, Alex Falck-03, Kapitän Engler-02)							

Coastal towage around the south coast of England

H & S MARINE SERVICES
Welvarend Hoop, The Quay, Burnham-on-Crouch, Essex, CM0 8AS
Livery - Orange hull with black trim and white wheelhouse

HAM		14,15	4,55	1,70		
(ex Pushycat 46)						
HERMAN JUNIOR	1979	15,12	4,66	2,10	565	5.4
(ex En Avant 9-03, Zal 4 -80)						
HERMAN SENIOR	1976	15,85	4,40	2,00	500	7.0

The HERMAN JUNIOR, with the name written as HERMAN JR on the vessel, works at Boston on 22 May 2004.

(David Dixon)

HAMPSON MARINE TOWAGE
967 Oldham Road, Rochdale, Lancs, OL16 4SE
Tel : 01706 640143   Mobile : 07835 851096

SEAPORT ALPHA	1943	54	19,80	5,18	2,43	280	5.5
(ex Tideall-86, TID 43 -49)						

Towage services at Fleetwood

Leaving Fleetwood at the start of her voyage to Larne on 20 July 2003 is the EUROPEAN LEADER. Meanwhile, work continues on the SEAPORT ALPHA which has been beached for some attention.

(Malcolm Slater)

HARWICH HAVEN AUTHORITY
Harbour House, The Quay, Harwich, Essex, CO12 3HH
Tel : 01255 243030   Fax : 01255 241302
E-mail : harbour.house@hha.co.uk
Website : www.hha.co.uk

HAVEN HORNBILL	2002		20,20	8,24	1,40	1104	12.0

HERBOSCH-KIERE MARINE CONTRACTORS LTD
Dundee House, Albion Place, Ramsgate, Kent, CT11 8HQ
Tel : 01843 583338   Fax : 01843 852670
E-mail : ramsgate@herbosch-kiere.demon.co.uk
Website : www.herbosch-kiere.demon.co.uk
Livery - Black hull with mustard housing

JOYCE	1972	107	17,65	5,61	2,80	340	3.2
TASK ONE	1973/96	147	26,00	8,00	2,10	580	8.0

Marine civil engineering around the UK coast
Part of the Soficom Group

HEYSHAM BOAT CHARTER LTD

1 Bazil Grove, Overton, Morecambe, Lancs, LA3 3JD
Tel : 01524 858354   Mobile : 07831 547117 or 07831 547118
E-mail : heyboat@aol.com
Livery - Black hull and white housing

SEA TROJAN	1963	117	24,00	7,00	3,25	850	14.0

Coastal towage services

Originally built for work at Aberdeen, and still registered there, the SEA TROJAN lies in her present base port of Heysham on 13 September 2003.

(Roy Cressey)

HOLYHEAD TOWING COMPANY LTD

Newry Beach Yard, Holyhead, Anglesey, LL65 1LB
Tel : 01407 760111   Fax : 01407 764531
E-mail : towing@holyhead.co.uk
Website : www.holyhead.co.uk
Livery - Black hull with white housing; red funnel with company badge

AFON ALAW	2004	200	25,50	9,00	2,40	2600	35.0
AFON BRAINT	2005	200	25,50	9,00	2,40	2600	35.0
AFON CEFNI	2002	101	22,50	7,50	2,00	1280	17.0
AFON GOCH	1997	129	23,80	7,50	2,00	1450	19.0
AFON LAS	1982	94	22,15	6,80	2,80	1350	18.0
(ex El Marzouk-00, Mirjam-91, Hydrex II-91, Claire-87)							
AFON WEN	1984	60	19,55	6,60	2,40	1040	15.0
(ex Wyeguard-00, Antje-97)							
LLANDDWYN ISLAND	1994	114	21,50	7,80	2,00	940	14.0
NORTH STACK	1984	15	13,30	4,80	1,50	430	6.0
(ex Kinnel-03, Kinghow-02)							

Coastal towage and marine civil engineering around Europe

ISLE OF MAN GOVERNMENT (DEPARTMENT OF TRANSPORT, HARBOURS DIVISION)

Sea Terminal Building, Douglas, Isle of Man, IM1 2RF
Tel : 01624 686628
Livery - Black hull, white housing; white funnel with government emblem

TARROO USHTEY	1997		15,00	6,00	1,50	600	6.0

Towage and marine services at Douglas and surrounding coastline

The TARROO USHTEY was photographed alongside the quay at Ramsey on 14 May 2005.
(Iain McCall)

ITCHEN MARINE (TOWAGE) LTD

American Wharf, Elm Street, Southampton, SO14 5GA
Tel : 023 8063 1500   Fax : 023 8033 5606
Livery - Black hull with light blue trim, buff housing and wheelhouse; red funnel with blue and black stripes

WYEFORCE	1993	57	19,20	6,10	2,60	1348	18.3
WYEFUEL	1973	50	16,70	5,20	2,80	330	3.0
(ex Wyeplay, Nancy)							
WYEPULL	1985	48	15,30	5,10	2,20	600	8.0
WYEPUSH	1989	50	14,50	5,10	2,10	750	8.0
WYETOW	1991	52	16,05	5,30	2,40	940	10.6

Towage services at Southampton

JENKINS MARINE LTD
Unit 12, Dawkins Road Industrial Estate, Poole, Dorset, BH15 4JP
Tel : 01202 668558   Fax : 01202 669209
E-mail : office@rjmarine.co.uk
Website : www.jenkinsmarine.co.uk

KINGSTON LACY	1960	75	21,00	6,00	2,60	495	7.0

(ex Kingston Buci-84)

Marine civil engineering support around the UK

JERSEY HARBOURS DEPARTMENT
Maritime House, La Rue du Port Elizabeth, St Helier, Jersey, JE1 1RB
Tel : 01534 885588   Fax : 01534 885599
E-mail : harbourmaster@jersey-harbours.com
Website : www.jersey-harbours.com

DUKE OF NORMANDY	2005	161	26,08	9,10	2,60	2200	30.0

Towage and marine services in Jersey and along the surrounding coast

KING'S LYNN CONSERVANCY BOARD
Harbour Office, Common Staith, King's Lynn, Norfolk, PE30 1LL
Tel : 01553 773411   Fax : 01553 763431
E-mail : harbourmaster@portauthoritykingslynn.fsnet.co.uk
Website : www.portauthoritykingslynn.fsnet.co.uk
Livery - Black hull with white wheelhouse

CONSERVATOR	2003		16,65	5,29	2,30	1080	14.2

Towage and marine services at King's Lynn

KLYNE TUGS (LOWESTOFT) LTD
Cumberland Place, Whapload Road, Lowestoft, Suffolk, NR32 1UQ
Tel : 01502 515250/565610   Fax : 01502 500225
E-mail : inquiries@klyne-tugs.demon.co.uk
Livery - White hull with red and blue "coastguard" stripe, cream superstructure; buff funnel with KTL in green letters

ANGLIAN MONARCH	1998	1485	58,00	14,10	6,90	11400	152.0
ANGLIAN PRINCE	1980	1598	69,06	14,86	6,14	11280	170.0
(ex Hispania-96, Salvageman-91)							
ANGLIAN PRINCESS	2002	2270	67,40	15,50	6,20	16400	180.0
ANGLIAN SOVEREIGN	2003	2500	67,40	15,50	6,20	16400	180.0

Maritime and Coastguard Agency emergency towing vessels

J P KNIGHT (CALEDONIAN) LTD

37 Shore Road, Invergordon, Ross-shire, IV18 0EQ
Tel : 01349 852611   Fax : 01349 853087
E-mail : fraser.forbes@jpknight.com
Website : www.jpknight.com
Livery - Red and black hull, brown housing and white wheelhouse; black funnel with white K

KINCRAIG	1998	290	31,00	9,80	3,50	3600	50.0
KINNAIRD	2003	312	36,00	9,50	3,21	4200	
(ex Iwaki Maru-05)							
KINROSS	1978	347	36,35	9,02	3,50	3200	48.0
(ex Fuji Maru-81)							

Towage services on the Cromarty Firth

J P KNIGHT GROUP LTD

Admiral's Offices, Main Gate Road, Chatham Historic Dockyard, Kent, ME4 4TZ
Tel : 01634 826633   Fax : 01634 829093
Website : www.jpknight.com
Livery - Black hull with white housing; black funnel with white K

KENLEY	1996	327	25,96	9,57	3,04	2400	
(ex EMS Express-04, Mack)							
KENNET	1981	282	24,26	8,32		4800	
(ex Terese Marie)							
KESSOCK	1975	233	28,35	9,35	3,88	2400	35.0
KINDEACE	1978	557	41,41	10,85	4,40	5000	70.0
(ex IJsland-88)							
KINLOCH	1974	233	28,35	9,35	3,88	2400	35.0
KUTARI	1991	192	18,00	9,47	2,40	2500	

Towage and pusher services in South America

LAXEY TOWING COMPANY LTD

Cloenstones Cottage, Baldrine, Isle of Man, IM4 6DS
Tel / fax : 01624 617436; after hours : 01624 861724
Livery - Black hull with brown housing, white wheelhouse; funnel black over white over red with black letter L on white

WENDY ANN	1934	72	23,10	5,48	2,25	600	8.0
(ex Vespa-74, Evelene Brodstone-35, Brodstone-34)							
LONAN	1976	8	9,14	3,35	1,37	200	3.0
(ex Lagan-99, Veronica-97)							

Towage services at Isle of Man ports

LERWICK PORT AUTHORITY
Albert Building, Lerwick, Shetland, ZE1 0LL
Tel : 01595 692991   Fax : 01595 693452
E-Mail : info@lerwick-harbour.co.uk
Website : www.lerwick-harbour.co.uk
Livery - Black hull with white housing

| KEBISTER | 1990 | 143 | 24,00 | 7,60 | 3,85 | 1760 | 24.0 |
| KNAB | 1980 | 71 | 18,60 | 6,10 | 2,80 | 460 | 7.0 |

Towage and pilotage services at Lerwick

D LITTLE ENGINEERING LTD
The Barn, Summer Hill, Freystrop, Haverfordwest, SA62 4LQ
Tel : 01437 890804   Fax : 01437 891315
E-mail : davelittle@btinternet.com
Website : www.dlittleengineering.co.uk
Livery - Black hull with white wheelhouse

DEFENCE	1987/99	124	25,00	6,60	3,00	500	7.0
(ex Angary-87)							
INTREPID B	1997/2002	181	27,00	8,80	5,50	1285	20.0
(ex Harvest Reaper III-02)							

PORT OF LONDON AUTHORITY
Head Office : Baker's Hall, 7 Harp Lane, London EC3R 6LB
Tel : 020 7743 7900
Marine Services : Denton Wharf, Mark Lane, Gravesend Kent, DA12 2QB
Tel : 01474 562444   Fax : 01474 562403
Website : www.portoflondon.co.uk
Livery - Green hull, cream wheelhouse with orange band around top of wheelhouse

| IMPULSE | 1995 | 52 | 14,00 | | 1,50 | 470 | 5.6 |

Towage and marine services on the River Thames

LONDONDERRY PORT & HARBOUR COMMISSIONERS
Harbour Office, Port Road, Lisahally, Londonderry, Co, Londonderry, BT47 1FL
Tel : 028 71860555   Fax : 028 71861168
E-mail : lderryport@aol.com
Website : www.londonderryport.com
Livery - Black hull with white wheelhouse

COULMORE	1982	290	33,18	9,63	4,17	2640	42.0
(ex Ganges-05)							
OTTERBANK	1996	120	16,89	5,29	1,70	800	11.4
SHROVE	2000	112	17,00	8,00	4,45	2636	34.0
(ex Bergslep-03)							

Harbour towage and pilot boat services at Londonderry

MAGNUS GROUP LTD
Cliff Reach, Cliff Road, Ipswich, Suffolk, IP3 6PB
Tel : 01473 281888   Fax : 01473 226743
Livery - Black hull with white housing and wheelhouse

TAYRA	1958	69	20,00	7,50	2,80		7.5

(ex Abeille No. 13-87, Patmore, Tayra)

MARINECO UK LTD
The Steading, Pentland Mains, Edinburgh, EH20 9QG
Tel : 0131 445 2345   Fax : 0131 445 4418
E-Mail : info@mcoukcom
Website : www.mcouk.com
Livery - Black hull, yellow housing with white wheelhouse

BALOO	2002		21,00	8,04	2,40	1280	16.0
(ex Mariska 2-03)							
MARINECO INDIA	1993		19,50	6,00	2,10	880	14.5
(ex Oil Randan-05)							
MARINECO RAKSHAA	1993	160	19,95	9,52	2,10	1400	18.0
(ex Smit Bison-04, DH Alpha-03)							
TABRIKI	1990		15,00	5,00	1,20	640	8.0

Coastal towage and marine civil engineering around Europe

MARITIME CRAFT SERVICES (CLYDE) LTD
Largs Yacht Haven, Irvine Road, Largs, Ayrshire, KA30 8EZ
Tel : 01475 675338   Fax : 01475 689000
E-mail : charter@maritimecraft.co.uk
Website : www.maritimecraft.co.uk
Livery - Black hull, Baltic blue bulwarks, white housing

MCS AILSA	1996	497	42,00	14,50	2,00	2000	22.0
(ex Katliz-03)							
MCS ANNEKE	1999	94	20,20	8,04	1,81	1200	12.5
(ex Mariska V-01)							
MCS ELLY	1997	196	25,40	10,15	2,30	1200	16.5
(ex DH Charlie-02)							
MCS LENIE	1997	121	24,00	9,00	2,75	2200	27.0
MCS MARLENE	2001	141	25,80	8,50	2,40	1950	24.5
(ex Shoalworker-02)							
MCS NIKKI	2004	161	26,08	9,10	2,60	2200	30.0
SHAKESPEARE	1988	32	15,30	4,78	1,50	760	8.0

Coastal towage and marine civil engineering services

McCRAE MARINE SERVICES
Nigg, Tain, Ross-shire, IV19 1QU
Tel : 01631 740206

KATHLEEN	1973	60	18,28	5,26	2,59	330	3.3

JOHN McLOUGHLIN & SON (SHIPPING) LTD

North End, Larne Harbour, Larne, County Antrim, BT40 1AJ
Tel : 028 2827 3785 / 028 2827 4085 (After hours : 028 9085 4701)   Fax : 028 2826 0382
Divis Berth, Northern Road, Belfast, BT3 9AL
Tel : 028 9085 4701
E-mail : mail@johnmcloughlinshipping.co.uk
Website : www.johnmcloughlinshipping.co.uk
Livery - Orange hull with white lettering, white housing; orange funnel with two white bands.

ADRIENNE McLOUGHLIN	1970	16	11,00	3,75	1,50	175	2.0
DAVID McLOUGHLIN	1971	22	14,00	3,75	1,75	250	6.0
DEIRDRE McLOUGHLIN	1980	16	11,00	3,50	1,75	175	3.0
DONNA McLOUGHLIN	1975	35	16,10	4,00	2,00	380	7.0
ELIZABETH McLOUGHLIN	1978	16	11,00	3,50	1,75	175	3.0
LEANNE McLOUGHLIN	2005	32	15,00	4,00	2,10	400	6.0
MARIA McLOUGHLIN	1981	35	16,00	4,50	2,10	500	8.0
MARY-ANN McLOUGHLIN	1972	21	14,00	3,75	1,00	150	1.5
MICHAEL McLOUGHLIN	1978	39	16,33	5,01	2,60	624	10.0
(ex Maura, Argus B-00, Glenesk)							
NOLEEN McLOUGHLIN	2005	32	15,00	4,00	2,10	400	6.0
PATRICIA McLOUGHLIN	1973	10	9,20	2,50	0,50	250	1.5
SAMUEL F McLOUGHLIN	1964	216	32,72	8,56	3,20	1300	20.0
(ex Hornby-84, J H Lamey-70)							
SARAH McLOUGHLIN	1981	35	16,00	4,50	2,10	500	8.0

Towage and line handling services in Belfast, Belfast Lough and Larne

The SAMUEL F McLOUGHLIN, her name written as SAMUEL F, is the largest vessel in the owner's fleet and originally worked on the River Mersey. She was photographed at Larne on 17 August 1992.

(Aubrey Dale)

The two latest additions to the McLoughlin fleet, NOLEEN McLOUGHLIN and LEANNE McLOUGHLIN, were photographed on a sunny July evening at their builder's yard in Bristol.
(Bernard McCall)

MEDWAY PORTS AUTHORITY
Sheerness Docks, Sheerness, Kent, ME12 1RS
Tel : 01795 596596   Fax : 01795 680072
E-mail : guypeto@medwayports.com
Livery - Black hull and housing with orange wheelhouse

MEDWAY OTTER	1973	21	15,50	4,30	1,75	153	0.8

Marine services on the River Medway

MEDWAY TOWING SERVICES
Rookshill House, Bitchet Green, Sevenoaks, Kent, TN15 0NG
Tel : 01732 761945   Fax : 01732 761957   Mobile : 07831 168996
Livery - Black hull, brown housing with white wheelhouse; green funnel with white band.

SILVERBEAM	1951	92	25,51	6,40	2,93	800	9.0

  (ex Jean Raby-03, Mercedes II-83, Silverbeam-71)

Marine civil engineering support and light towage services on the River Medway.

MERSEY MARINE LTD
177 Kings Road, Higher Bebington, Wirral, CH63 8QZ
Tel : 0151 200 3189   Fax : 0151 609 1924
E-mail : williamsptrs@aol.com

MERSEY ONE	1971	20	14,45	4,28	1,80	365	4.0

Late News: This vessel now sold

GUY & MIDGE MIDDLETON
Lowestoft

JACK ROSE	1958	68	18,29	5,79	2,82	440	6.0

(ex Martello-02)

Vessel currently laid up

MILFORD HAVEN PORT AUTHORITY
PO Box 14, Gorsewood Drive, Milford Haven, SA73 3ER
Tel : 01646 696100   Fax : 01646 696125
E-mail : enquiries@mhpa.co.uk
Website : www.mhpa.co.uk

LILAH	1973	50	18,28	5,26	2,59	330	3.3

Towage services in Milford fish dock

MISTLEY MARINE & LEISURE LTD
Mistley Boatyard, Anchor Lane, Mistley, Manningtree, CO11 1NG
Tel : 01206 392127   Fax : 01206 396952

MERLIN	2005		20,00	7,50	1,50	550	8.0

Marine services on the east coast of England

MONTROSE PORT AUTHORITY
Harbour Office, South Quay, Ferryden, Montrose, Angus, DD10 9SL
Tel : 01674 672302   Fax : 01674 675530
E-mail : enquiries@montroseport.co.uk
Website : www.montroseport.co.uk
Livery - Light blue hull with white wheelhouse

GLENESK	1976	37	15,70	4,90	2,25	730	10.5

(ex Comar-99, Omar)

Towage services at Montrose

MURRAY TUGS (NORE MARITIME SHIPPING LTD)
8 Rushenden Road, Queenborough, Kent, ME11 5HB
Tel : 01795 580998   Fax : 01795 665534
E-mail : murraytugs@aol.com
Livery - Black hull, white housing and wheelhouse; red funnel

NORE CHALLENGER *	1973	184	31,55	8,60	4,20	2230	32.0
(ex Superbe-00, Guarne-78)							
NORE COMMODORE **	1961	147	28,65	7,39	3,66	1320	16.0
(ex Airedale-96)							
NORE CREST	1955	119	26,07	7,11	3,12	1100	12.0
(ex Alnwick-87)							

NORE SWALE (ex Prestwick-00)	1955	119	26,07	7,11	3,12	1100	12.0
NORE TRITON (ex Zephyr)	1964	50	16,70	5,30	2,80	500	5.0
PIONEER (ex Sandsfoot Castle-03, Elena B-96, Afon Goch-91, Karet-82)	1967	231	33,02	8,97	3,97	2250	35.0

* *Based Ramsgate for ferry berthing and coastal towage; flies Comoros Islands flag*

** *Based Newhaven for ferry berthing and coastal towage; flies Belize flag*

Other tugs provide towage services on the Rivers Medway and Thames; also coastal towage

The NORE COMMODORE catches the late evening sunlight at Newhaven on a warm evening in July 2003.

(Bernard McCall)

NORTHWEST STEAMSHIP CO LTD
E-mail : info@tugkerne.co.uk
Website : www.tugkerne.co.uk

KERNE (ex Terrier-47, Viking-13)	1912	63	23,47	5,48	2,59	400	

Preserved steam tug based at Ellesmere Port Boat Museum

OCARINIA SHIPPING
31 - 37 North Quay, Douglas, Isle of Man

FALMOUTH BAY (ex Karew Castle-96, Carew Castle-94, Thorngarth-91)	1959	284	39,00	9,00	3,70	1300	

This vessel believed to be a total loss and the Company sold.

OFFSHORE WORKBOATS LTD
Primrose Quay, Ferry Road, Renfrew, PA4 8SH
Tel : 0141 886 1212   Fax : 0141 886 3510
E-mail : offshore@tiscali.co.uk

BARRACUDA BAY	1970		13,30	4,00	1,50	220	3.0
BARROW SAND	1970	79	19,50	6,70	1,70	480	5.0
MARIE JOSE	1974		14,15	4,55	1,70	365	4.1
(ex Pushycat)							
TORBROOK	1961	13	12,50	3,40	1,60	120	1.4
(ex Tregarth-90, Shalldo-72)							
TRIO	1972		14,50	4,30	1,80	380	4.2
TROJAN	1976	33	14,17	4,57	2,37	460	5.5
(ex Conservator-03, Junior-93)							

Towage and marine services on the River Clyde
Late News: MARIE JOSE sold to Irish owners

ORKNEY ISLANDS COUNCIL
Department of Harbours, Harbour Authority Building, Scapa, Orkney, KW15 1SD
Tel : 01856 873636   Fax : Tel : 01856 873012
E-mail : harbours@orkney.gov.uk
Website : www.orkneyharbours.com

KIRKWALL BAY	1992	57	17,25	5,19	2,00	899	9.5

Towage and pilot launch services at Kirkwall

ORKNEY TOWAGE COMPANY LTD
Harbour Authority Building, Scapa, Orkney, KW15 1SD
Tel : 01856 873636   Fax : 01856 877635
E-mail : orkneytowage@orkney.gov.uk
Website : www.orkneyharbours.com
Livery - Black hull with white housing; buff funnel with company emblem and a red main mast

EINAR	1989	410	31,50	10,00	4,78	4000	53.0
ERLEND	1990	410	31,50	10,00	4,78	4000	53.0
HARALD	1992	411	32,00	10,00	4,78	4000	55.0

Towage services at Flotta oil terminal in Scapa Flow

OSPREY SHIPPING LTD
Howden Terminal, Willington Quay, Wallsend, Tyne & Wear, NE28 6UL
Tel : 0191 234 5511   Fax : 0191 234 0888
E-mail : newcastle@ospreyltd.com
Website : www.ospreyltd.com

CUMBRAE	1961	152	28,65	7,39	3,66	1320	16.1
(ex Clutha-97, Alsatian-95)							

Coastal towage on the east coast of England

Osprey Shipping's tug CUMBRAE, formerly in the RMAS fleet, sails down the River Tyne on 19 April 2005.

(Dominic McCall)

J T PALMER MARINE SERVICES

Katrina Wharf, Wharf Road, Gravesend, Kent, DA12 2RU
Tel : 01474 567730
Livery - Black hull with green housing and white wheelhouse; blue funnel with large white P

UNICO	1927	51	17,70	4,75	2,13	200	3.0

Marine services on the River Thames and River Medway

The veteran tug UNICO makes a cautious approach to Tilbury on 23 May 2004.

(Ian Willett)

PLANTAIN (UK) LTD, trading as PLANTAIN MARINE

Empire Wharf, The Docks, Falmouth, Cornwall, TR11 4NR
Tel : 01326 312987   Fax : 01326 312564
E-mail : jon@validfal.fsnet.co.uk
Livery - Black hull with white housing and orange trim (Doris K)
        Orange hull with white wheelhouse (Valid)

DORIS K	1969	77	22,10	6,25	2,56	600	8.0
(ex Doris-90)							
VALID	1990	21	12,80	4,20	1,70	286	3.5

Towage and marine services in Falmouth

POOLE HARBOUR COMMISSIONERS

20 New Quay Road, Hamworthy, Poole, Dorset, BH15 4AF
Tel : 01202 440200   Fax : 01202 440212
E-mail : pooleharbourcommissioners@phc.co.uk
Website : www.phc.co.uk
Livery - Dark green hull with yellow housing and white wheelhouse

HERBERT BALLAM	1998	63	18,25	6,00	2,40	1300	19.0

Towage services at Poole

PORT TALBOT DIVING & MARINE

45 Sitwell Way, Port Talbot, West Glamorgan, SA12 8BP
Tel : 01639 884766   Fax : 01792 459550
E-mail : info@ptmarine.co.uk
Website : www.ptmarine.co.uk
Livery - Black hull, red wheelhouse with white trim

ALEC D	1960	130	18,28	10,97	1,80	1200	12.0
BOY EUAN	1972	20	11,23	4,18	1,60	240	2.0
G-WIZ	1974	25	15,24	4,34	1,90	480	6.0
(ex G.W. 226)							
STRATHDOON	1980	31	18,23	5,18	2,80	380	6.0

Towage and marine services at Port Talbot

PORTLAND TOWAGE LTD

Portland Port, Castletown, Portland, DT5 1PP
Tel : 01305 824044   Fax : 01305 824055
E-mail : info@portland-port.co.uk
Website : www.portland-port.co.uk
Livery - Black hull with white housing and wheelhouse

RUFUS CASTLE	1963	152	28,65	7,39	3,66	1320	16.1
(ex Bassett Hound-98, Bassett-95)							
SANDSFOOT CASTLE	1965	152	28,65	7,39	3,66	1320	16.1
(ex Dalmatian-03)							

WYKE CASTLE	1980	179	26,03	7,95	2,39	1600	27.0

(ex Pullman-04, Kiso Maru-03)
Harbour towage at Portland; also coastal towage

RIGG SHIPPING
31 Berkeley Close, Ipswich, IP4 2TS
Tel : 01473 434097

LOWGARTH	1965	152	28,96	7,60	3,66	920	15.0

Marine services around Ipswich

RIVER TEES ENGINEERING
The Slipways, Dockside Road, Middlesbrough, TS3 8AT
Tel : 01642 226226   Fax : 01642 245544
E-mail : river-tees@the-slipways.fsnet.co.uk
Website : www.river-tees-engineering.com

LIBRA STAR	1965	43	18,00	5,00	1,83	260	5.0

(ex Arco Deben-92)
Marine services on the River Tees

ROSYTH MARINE SERVICES LTD
Building 1058, Middle Jetty Road, Rosyth Royal dockyard, Fife, KY11 2YD
Tel : 01383 422450   Fax : 01383 423184
E-mail : tugs2000@rosyth.fsbusiness.co.uk
Livery - Red hull with white housing and wheelhouse
        Black hull with blue housing; white funnel (Babcock vessels)

ISABEL	1972	50	18,20	5,20	2,57	330	3.5
ST. MARGARET	1967	143	26,52	7,68	3,20	1200	15.0

(ex Inchcolm-89)

Managed for Babcock Rosyth Defence Ltd (UK)

DEERHOUND	1966	151	28,68	7,72	3,20	1770	17.0
ELKHOUND	1966	151	28,68	7,72	3,20	1770	17.0

Towage services at Rosyth

SEAHAM HARBOUR DOCK COMPANY
Cargo Durham Distribution Centre, Seaham, Co. Durham, SR7 7NZ
Tel: 0191 516 1700   Fax: 0191 516 1701
E-mail : info@portofseaham.com
Livery - Light blue hull, white wheelhouse with buff mast

SEAHAM PRIDE	1975	42	15,09	4,68	1,40	720	7.2

(ex Henry Boy-80)
Towage services at Seaham

SERCO-DENHOLM LTD

Victory Court, Cartsburn, Greenock, PA15 4RT
Tel : 01475 787912   Fax : 01475 731539
Livery - Red hull with white wheelhouse and blue funnel or black hull with buff housing and funnel

ATLAS	1999	168	21,30	7,80	2,40	2100	33.0
(ex Yenikale-05)							
GEORGINA	1973	143	21,95	6,40	2,59	615	5.7
GWENDOLINE P	1974	143	21,95	6,40	2,59	615	5.7
(ex Gwendoline-99)							

The latest addition to the Serco-Denholm fleet in Portsmouth is the ATLAS, built and previously owned in Turkey. She is seen here at Portsmouth on 14 June 2005.

(Danny Lynch)

Operated for Ministry of Defence (Navy Department)

ADEPT	1980	384	38,79	9,40	4,20	2640	29.6
BUSTLER	1981	384	38,79	9,40	4,20	2640	29.6
CAPABLE	1981	384	38,79	9,40	4,20	2640	29.6
DEXTEROUS	1986	384	38,79	9,40	4,20	2640	29.6
FAITHFUL	1985	384	38,79	9,40	4,20	2640	29.6
FORCEFUL	1985	384	38,79	9,40	4,20	2640	29.6
NIMBLE	1985	384	38,79	9,40	4,20	2640	29.6
POWERFUL	1985	384	38,79	9,40	4,20	2640	29.6

Operated for RMAS

CAREFUL	1982	384	38,79	9,40	4,20	2640	29.6
FLORENCE	1980	143	21,95	6,40	2,59	615	5.7
FRANCES	1980	143	21,95	6,40	2,59	615	5.7
GENEVIEVE	1980	143	21,95	6,40	2,59	615	5.7
HELEN	1974	143	21,95	6,40	2,59	615	5.7
HUSKY	1969	152	28,65	7,39	3,66	1320	16.1
IMPETUS	1993	319	32,53	10,42	4,00	3400	38.6
IMPULSE	1993	319	32,53	10,42	4,00	3400	38.6
KITTY	1972	60	18,28	5,26	2,59	330	3.0
LESLEY	1973	60	18,28	5,26	2,59	330	3.0
MYRTLE	1973	60	18,28	5,26	2,59	330	3.0
SALUKI	1969	152	28,65	7,39	3,66	1320	20.0
SETTER	1969	152	28,65	7,39	3,66	1320	16.1
SHEEPDOG	1969	152	28,65	7,39	3,66	1320	16.1
SPANIEL	1967	152	28,65	7,39	3,66	1320	16.1

Towage services for the Ministry of Defence

The International Festival of the Sea, held at Portsmouth in July 2005, provided many opportunities to observe warships and auxiliary vessels. The SHEEPDOG is seen here assisting the French auxiliary MEUSE.

(Bernard McCall)

SHETLAND TOWAGE LTD
Sella Ness Industrial Estate, Graven, Mossbank, Shetland, ZE2 9UR
Tel : 01806 242708   Fax : 01806 242272
E-mail : info@shetland-towage.co.uk
Website : www.shetland-towage.co.uk
Livery - Red hull with red housing; black funnel

DUNTER	1996	797	38,37	13,40	5,98	5760	55.0
SHALDER	1983	538	37,33	11,30	5,40	4000	45.0
TIRRICK	1983	538	37,33	11,30	5,40	4000	45.0
TYSTIE	1996	797	38,37	13,40	5,98	5760	55.0
Royal Bank Leasing Ltd							
STANECHAKKER	1978	423	37,25	10,00	5,40	3800	54.0

Towage services at Sullom Voe oil terminal

The TIRRICK is seen in the Shetland oil port of Sullom Voe on 21 February 2005.

(Dominic McCall)

SHOREHAM PORT AUTHORITY
Harbour Office, 84 - 86 Albion Street, Southwick, Brighton, BN42 4ED
Tel : 01273 598100   Fax : 01273 592492
Website : www.portshoreham.co.uk

ADURNI	1984	40	15,70	4,80	2,20	720	10.0

SMIT (SCOTLAND) LTD
Regent Centre, Regent Road, Aberdeen, AB11 5NS
Tel : 01224 560400   Fax : 01224 581485

SMIT ARROL	2000	36	12,00	3,84	1,55	141	1.4
SMIT BAKER	2000	36	12,00	3,84	1,55	141	1.4
SMIT FOWLER	2000	36	12,00	3,84	1,55	141	1.4

Line-handling services at the Hound Point oil terminal in the Firth of Forth

SOLENT TOWAGE LIMITED
Esso Fawley Marine Terminal, PO Box 43, Hythe, Hampshire, SO4 6WF
Tel : 01703 891554   Fax : 01703 891552
Website : www.ostensjo.no
Livery - Navy blue hull with light blue housing; navy blue funnel with white band and company logo

ASTERIX	2001	31	13,00	4,80	3,00	552	9.5
IBEX	1993	33	14,40	4,73	1,50	600	7.8
SILEX	1994	543	35,11	11,45	5,02	5000	62.0
THRAX	1994	543	35,11	11,45	5,02	5000	62.0

Towage services at the Fawley oil terminal

SPECIALIST MARINE SERVICES LTD

Ocean House, Waterside Park, Livingstone Road, Hessle, HU13 0EG
Tel : 01482 350999   Fax : 01482 648284
E-mail : info@smstowage.com
Website : www.smstowage.com
Livery - Red hull and white housing; red funnel
Managers for SMS Towage Ltd

NORMAN	1981	298	32,85	9,50	4,00	3200	50.0
(ex Hozan Maru-03, Minase Maru-00, Nagato Maru-96)							
RIVERMAN	1977	78	18,50	5,80	2,60	730	12.0
(ex Bogoy-03, Skorpo-01)							
SERVICEMAN	1984	194	31,35	9,50	3,20	3500	54.5
(ex Shinano Maru-03)							
TRADESMAN	1987	182	22,80	9,15	3,70	2600	35.0
(ex Waglan-03)							
TRUEMAN	1987	182	22,61	9,15	3,50	2600	35.0
(ex Tai Tam-03)							

Towage services at Hull, Grimsby and Immingham

Sunny but cold winter days make good conditions for photography. The date is 29 December 2003 and the TRADESMAN is at work in Grimsby.

(David Dixon)

SPITHEAD TRADING CO
(TOWAGE & MARINE CONSTRUCTION CONTRACTORS)
Gosfield Eaves, Gosfield Road, Braintree, Essex, CM7 5PA
Tel : 01787 472098   Fax : 01787 472098
Livery - Black hull, sky blue housing with red trim and white wheelhouse

DUCKETT	1938		16,15	3,96	1,52	180	2.5
GLUVIAS	1959	207	32,36	8,51	3,54	1260	22.0
(ex St Gluvias-05, Cruiser-81, Clonmel-73)							
GOLIATH	1956	169	28,73	7,65	3,80	1290	17.0
(ex M.S.C. Scimitar)							

Marine civil engineering services and coastal towage

The GOLIATH is seen assisting a barge at Great Yarmouth.

(Martin Penwright)

THE STEAM TUG PORTWEY TRUST
'Tether's End', Old London Road, Rawreth, Wickford, Essex, SS11 8UE
E-mail : portweytug@aol.com
Website-www.stportwey.co.uk

PORTWEY	1927	94	24,54	5,48	2,74	330

Preserved tug berthed in West India Dock, London

STEAM TUG TID 172
E-mail : tidtug@globalnet.co.uk
Website : www.users.globalnet.co.uk/~tidtug

TID 172	1946	54	22,55	5,18	1,82	220
(ex Pallion-73, TID 172-48)						

Preserved steam tug berthed at Mistley

SURVEY & SUPPLY (GRIMSBY)

14 Denby Drive, Cleethorpes, Lincolnshire, DN35 9QQ
Tel : 07836 310384   Fax : 01472 340020
Livery - Black hull, white housing and wheelhouse; black and white funnel

Operated for R J Harvey

INGE	1962	143	23,78	7,88	3,60	1300	11.5
(ex Stedingen-96)							
JADI	1968	143	25,56	7,88	3,60	1300	11.5
(ex Butjadingen-96)							
JOAN	1965	125	26,03	7,77	3,80	1600	16.0
(ex Lady Joan-01, Langland-98, Burma-94, Plasma-91)							
ESTE	1973	196	29,67	8,06	2,65	1800	22.0
(ex Geeste-05, Midgard 1-03)							
LADY	1965	125	26,70	7,80	3,80	1600	16.0
(ex Lady Theresa-01, Caswell-98, Dhulia-94, Platoon-93)							

Harbour towage at Grimsby

The JOAN spent her early years working in London's enclosed docks and she remains a useful vessel for shiphandling in confined areas. She is seen at Grimsby on 5 May 2002.

(David Dixon)

SVITZER MARINE LIMITED

Tees Wharf, Dockside Road, Middlesbrough, TS3 6AB
Tel : 01642 258300   Fax : 01642 246370
E-mail : tees@svitzer.com
Website : www.svitzer.com
Livery - Dark blue hull, cream housing with white or cream upperworks; dark blue funnel with black top and white band bearing dark blue 'Maltese' cross

SEA ENDEAVOUR	1980	221	30,48	9,05	3,62	3150	42.0

Currently laid up and for sale at Swansea

Based on the River Tyne

FLYING SPINDRIFT	1986	259	30,66	9,43	3,40	3100	40.0
ROWANGARTH	1981	382	34,24	10,04	3,23	3200	42.0
YARM CROSS	1979	207	28,30	9,00	2,76	2640	35.5

Normally working on the River Tees, the ROSEBERRY CROSS was transferred to work on the River Tyne in summer 2005 in order to deputise for the YARM CROSS whilst the latter tug was in drydock. Tynemouth is the attractive setting for the ROSEBERRY CROSS as she heads out to meet an incoming vessel.

(Dominic McCall)

Based on the River Tees

AYTON CROSS	2000	433	33,00	11,90	3,90	4400	60.0
COATHAM CROSS	1981	185	28,30	9,00	2,76	2640	35.0
FIERY CROSS	1993	296	30,58	10,33	2,66	3890	42.0
ORMESBY CROSS	2000	433	33,00	11,90	3,90	4400	60.0
PHOENIX CROSS	1993	296	30,58	10,33	2,66	3890	42.0
ROSEBERRY CROSS	1989	290	30,58	10,33	2,56	3382	37.0

Based at Grangemouth

CARRON	1979	225	28,45	8,92	2,90	2200	24.0
CLEVELAND CROSS	1989	290	30,58	10,33	2,56	3382	37.0

Based at Avonmouth/Portbury

AVONGARTH	1980	189	32,07	9,20	2,50	2600	35.0
(ex Iwashima Maru-91)							
FORAGER	1988	44	16,50	5,30	2,40	886	13.0
(ex Afon Wen-99, Frances-94)							

The FORAGER joined the Avonmouth fleet in June 2005 after a career which has seen her work in various parts of the UK and overseas. Her main roles now are to undertake plough dredging in Bristol's City Docks and to escort large vessels in the River Avon. She was photographed in this river as she made her way back to Avonmouth after her first duty - escorting a visiting warship to Bristol on 10 June 2005.

(Chris Jones)

PORTGARTH	1995	262	30,70	10,04	4,10	3980	50.0
STACKGARTH	1985	216	28,29	8,95	4,80	3400	43.0
(ex Eston Cross-94)							
SVITZER BRISTOL	2003	366	29,50	11,00	5,90	4338	60.0
SVITZER BRUNEL	2003	366	29,50	11,00	5,90	4338	60.0
WESTGARTH	1983	266	32,11	9,90	2,92	3000	40.0
(ex Yashima-92)							
Based at Newport/Cardiff/Barry							
BARGARTH	1979	225	28,43	8,92	2,97	2200	24.0
(ex Forth-03, Laggan-87)							
HALLGARTH	1979	223	29,47	8,94	2,91	2190	23.0
HOLMGARTH	1979	223	28,45	8,94	2,91	2190	23.0
Based at Swansea/Port Talbot							
BATTLEAXE	1978	423	37,98	10,55	4,38	3800	54.0
(ex Elsie-98, Lyrie-96)							
HURRICANE H	1970	282	33,91	9,45	4,80	2400	39.0
(ex Margam-97)							
SHIREEN S	1976	312	38,00	9,63	4,03	2640	35.0
(ex Kelty-98)							
YEWGARTH	1985	452	36,86	10,52	4,16	4000	50.0

Based at Milford Haven

ANGLEGARTH	1996	374	32,72	11,96	4,95	5100	66.0
MILLGARTH	1997	374	32,72	11,96	4,95	5100	66.0
SVITZER MILFORD	2004		33,30	11,50	4,80	4820	66.0

Based on the River Mersey

ASHGARTH	1992	307	36,50	10,20	4,70	3600	55.0
(ex Senho Maru-98)							
OAKGARTH	1984	452	36,86	10,52	4,16	4000	50.0
SHANNON	1981	382	34,27	10,06	3,85	3200	42.0
(ex Eldergarth-99)							
SVITZER BIDSTON	2004	366	29,50	11,00	5,90	4338	60.0
SVITZER BOOTLE	2004	366	29,50	11,00	5,90	4338	60.0
SVITZER (tbn)	2006		37,50	13,50		7200	70.0
THORNGARTH	1983	365	36,28	10,52	3,15	3400	45.0
(ex Tenzan-91)							

Based on the River Clyde

DALEGARTH	1985	298	38,00	10,27	3,15	3400	45.0
(ex Strongbow-91, Kestrel-90, Yokosuka Maru No.1-85)							
FLYING PHANTOM	1981	347	37,95	9,68	3,83	2820	43.0
SVITZER MULL	2005		30,00	11,50	4,80	5842	70.0
WARRIOR III	1975	227	29,65	8,62	2,30	2600	37.0
(ex Warrior-97, Celtic Warrior-96, Montenovo-93, Hayakuni Maru-91)							

Based at Belfast

COLERAINE	1970	245	32,19	8,87	3,61	2500	32.0
NORTON CROSS	1984	216	28,30	9,22	3,00	3400	43.5
WILLOWGARTH	1989	392	31,60	9,54	4,05	3400	45.0

Harbour towage at ports around the UK; also coastal towage

Part of the Svitzer-Wijsmuller Group

Late News: SEA ENDEAVOUR and SHIREEN S sold; OAKGARTH transferred to Swansea

Photographed in Milford Haven on 28 August 2004, the DALEGARTH was transferred north to Svitzer's Clyde fleet in early summer 2005.

(Danny Lynch)

TARGE TOWING LTD

Mountboy by Montrose, Angus, DD10 9TN
Tel : 01674 820234   Fax : 01674 820363
E-mail : ttl@targetowing.co.uk
Livery - Black hull with white housing and black funnel
        Black hull with white housing and black funnel with green band (BP Exploration)
        Green hull with white housing and red funnel with green and white bands
            (BP Shipping)

CARRICKFERGUS	1976	193	28,30	8,95	2,83	2200	27.0
(ex Greatham Cross-94)							
COLLIE T	1965	151	28,60	7,40	3,65	1320	20.0
(ex Te Awhina-03, Collie-01)							
CULTRA	1976	193	28,30	8,95	2,83	2200	27.0
(ex Skelton Cross-93)							
DEIRDRE	1968	122	28,92	7,62	2,81	1500	23.0

Towage services at Dundee, Aberdeen and Peterhead

Originally built for work on the River Tees, the CARRICKFERGUS was photographed as she arrived at Aberdeen on 2 July 2004.

(David Dodds)

Managed for BP Exploration Operating Co Ltd (UK)

CRAMOND	1994	449	34,30	10,50	4,60	4800	62.0
DALMENY	1994	449	34,30	10,50	4,60	4800	62.0
HOPETOUN	1997	947	43,50	14,20	6,04	9700	125.0

Towage services at Hound Point oil terminal on the Firth of Forth

Managed for BP Shipping Ltd (UK)

CASTLE POINT	2005	385	32,22	11,70	5,27	5445	66.7
CORRINGHAM	2005	385	32,22	11,70	5,27	5445	66.7
STANFORD	2005	385	32,22	11,70	5,27	5310	66.7

Towage services at Coryton oil terminal on the River Thames

Tilbury Cruise Terminal is the setting for the STANFORD on 16 April 2005.

(John Southwood)

The RED EMPRESS leaves Ayr with a timber barge in tow.

(Ken Stewart)

TAYLOR & TAYLOR
The Harbour, Troon, KA10 6DW
Tel : 01292 315489   Fax : 01292 317276
E-mail : rdtaylorandtaylor@hotmail.com
Livery - Black and red hull with dark blue housing, white wheelhouse with red band at top

RED COUNTESS	1983	31	16,17	4,84	2,00	500	5.0
(ex Curlew-02)							
RED EMPRESS	1968	77	22,10	6,25	2,50	495	6.0
(ex Daphne B-03, Daphne-01)							

Towage services at Troon and on the west coast of Scotland

TEIGNMOUTH HARBOUR COMMISSIONERS
2 Orchard Gardens, Teignmouth, Devon, TQ14 8DR
Tel : 01626 772376   Fax : 01626 770317
E-mail : thc@tozers.co.uk
Website : www.teignmouth-harbour.com
Livery - Light grey hull with white wheelhouse
Managed by Pike Ward Ltd

TEIGN C	1997	27	14,40	4,73	1,70	600	8.0

Towage services at Teignmouth, also plough dredging

THAMES & MEDWAY TOWAGE LTD
125 Queen Anne Avenue, Bromley, Kent, BR2 0SH
Tel : 020 84603620   Fax : 020 83139488
Livery - Black hull, white housing and black; red and white funnel

AICIRTON	1967	109	22,08	6,84	3,50		12.0
(ex Smit Amerika-89, Bartel Wilton)							
WARRIOR	1937	58	20,95	6,60	3,00	860	8.0
(ex General I-83, Vanoc-75)							

Towage services around the Thames estuary

TORBAY AND BRIXHAM SHIPPING AGENTS LIMITED
47 Overgang, Brixham, Devon, TQ5 8AR
Tel : 01803 882214   Fax : 01803 882579
E-mail : ops@tbsa.co.uk
Website : www.tbsa.co.uk
Livery - Black hull with white trim, red housing and wheelhouse with black trim

BAY PROTECTOR	1967	114	26,19	6,10	2,80	680	9.0
(ex Protector-95; HD 91-89; Wouter Johannis-84)							

Marine services at Brixham and Torbay

THE TRUSTEE OF HARBOURS OF PETERHEAD

Harbour Office, West Pier, Peterhead, AB42 1DW
Tel : 01779 483600   Fax : 01779 475715
E-mail : postmaster@peterhead-harbours.co.uk
Website : www.peterhead-harbours.co.uk

| FLYING SCUD | 1981 | 18 | 11,30 | 3,60 | 1,50 | 127 | 1.0 |

Towage services around Peterhead Fish Dock

The *FLYING SCUD* crosses Peterhead Bay on 7 December 2004.

(David Dodds)

TUG MANNING LTD

86 Ferndale Road, Gravesend, Kent, DA12 5AE
Mobile Tel : 017980 004489
Livery - Blue hull, white housing and wheelhouse with orange band

| MEECHING | 1960 | 173 | 29,27 | 7,70 | 3,11 | 1320 | 16.0 |

Coastal towage and dredging work around UK and Europe

TYNE TOWAGE MARINE LTD

Devlin Quay, Waggonway Road, Hebburn, Tyne & Wear, NE31 1SP
Tel : 0191 421881   Fax : 0191 4281909
E-mail : tyne.towage@svitzer.com

BANTAM	1955		7,62	3,65	2,13	150	4.0
PUSHY DEV	1956/93		12,19	5,34	2,32		
(ex Frederick Oldridge)							
SARAH D	1978	210	24,50	8,50	2,00	800	10.0
(ex Cleveland Endeavour-01)							

Marine support on the River Tyne and adjacent coast
Part of the Svitzer-Wijsmuller Group
Late News: SARAH D transferred to Svitzer Marine fleet in Milford Haven

UK DREDGING
Queen Alexandra House, Cargo Road, Cardiff, CF10 4LY
Tel : 02920 835200   Fax : 02920 835216
E-mail : ukd@abports.co.uk
Website : www.ukdredging.co.uk

UKD SEAHORSE	2000	206	25,97	10,06	2,55	1302	18.0
UKD SEALION	2003	224	25,97	10,06	2,55	1279	17.6

Marine civil engineering and dredging support around the UK

WCT OFFSHORE LTD
Hoist 13/14, King's Dock, Swansea, SA1 8QT
Tel : 01269 597614   Fax : 01269 595721
Livery - Black hull, white housing and red funnel with company logo

CAPT I. B. HARVEY	1992	182	29,30	8,60	3,40	1604	25.0
(ex Vic III-94, Vik III-93)							
I. B. SMITH	1992	182	29,30	8,60	3,40	1604	25.0
(ex Vic IV-94, Vik IV-93)							

Managed for Yale Invest & Finance (British Virgin Islands)

SIR MICHAEL	1973	475	42,30	11,16	4,64	4300	60.0
(ex Abu Samir-95, Cherdas-85, Bever-81)							

Managed for Purplewater Towing (British Virgin Islands)

GARIBALDO	2005	499	38,00	11,00	4,20		63.0
TIGRILLO	1972	264	28,72	8,80	4,76	2500	32.0
(ex Marseillais 15)							

Coastal towage around Europe
Late News: CAPT I. B. HARVEY and I. B. SMITH both sold

Normally based in the Solent, the WILANNE is seen at full speed in Milford Haven in April 2005.
(Danny Lynch)

WILLIAMS MARINE & PORT SERVICES LTD
The Royal Dockyard, Port of Pembroke, Pembroke Dock, SA72 6TD
Tel : 01646 692418   Fax : 01646 687153
E-mail : enquiries@wmps.co.uk
Website : www.wmps.co.uk
Dark blue hull with light blue trim and white wheelhouse

LISA	1965		12,00	3,20	1,50	250	2.5
SEAHORSE	1997	66	18,70	8,07	1,80	960	10.0
WILFREEDOM	1988	47	19,36	6,17	2,05	886	11.0

(ex Albatros 4-04; Albatros-03)
Towage and marine services at Milford Haven and in the Bristol Channel
A joint venture by Williams Shipping Marine Ltd and The Milford Docks Company

WILLIAMS SHIPPING MARINE LTD
Manor House Avenue, Millbrook, Southampton, SO15 0LF
Tel : 023 8023 7330   Fax : 023 8023 6151
E-mail : enquiries@williams-shipping.co.uk
Website : www.williams-shipping.co.uk
Livery - Dark blue hull with light blue trim and white wheelhouse

HOFLAND	1964	36	16,36	4,78	2,30	380	4.2
WILANNE	2004	36	16,89	5,29	2,25	960	12.8
WILCAT	1985	26	14,00	6,40	1,25	260	2.5
WILJAY	1973	12	12,65	3,36	1,50	380	3.5

(ex Copar-96)

WILFLOW	1977	25	14,06	6,06	0,90	320	3.0
WILPOWER	1995	51	19,60	6,04	2,35	960	13.1

(ex Karin S-05, Diamante-98)
Towage services at Southampton and along the south coast of England

PETER E WOODGER CRAFT HIRE
Woodger's Wharf, Horsham Lane, Rainham, Gillingham, Kent, ME8 7XB
Tel : 01634 374716   Fax : 01634 374509

FELAURA	1976	22	14,15	4,28	1,80	365	4.0

Towage and marine services in the Medway area

WORKINGTON PORT
Prince of Wales Dock, Workington, Cumbria, CA14 2JH
Tel: 01900 602301
E-mail : workington.port@cumbriacc.gov.uk
Website-www.portofworkington.co.uk
Livery- Black hull with blue bulwarks and white wheelhouse with orange trim

DERWENT	1992	120	16,89	5,29	2,00	722	10.5

Towage and pilot launch services at Workington

At the time of writing, ownership of the following tugs is uncertain.

ASSURANCE 1944 54 19,80 5,18 3,43
(ex Wyepress-94, Assurance-92, TID 71-64)
Based in Dublin

BONCHURCH 1944 63 22,25 5,18 1,82 380 8.0
(ex Baie Comeau-66, Abeille No.13-63, TID 174)
Lying at Leigh-on-Sea

FLYING CHILDERS 1976 330 38,10 9,60 4,00 2540 35.0
Lying at Greenock in damaged condition

HECTOR READ 1965 67 19,80 5,80 2,60 545 6.3

The HECTOR READ worked at Great Yarmouth for some 35 years before being purchased by Whiting Shipping whose colours she bore when photographed at Hull on 9 March 2003. She is of interest in being the last vessel built at the shipyard of J S Doig in Grimsby.

(David Dixon)

MAXIMUS 1956 141 29,00 7,10 3,20 750 8.0
Laid up at Lowestoft

MULTITUG II 1947/62 23,03 5,44 2,68 300
(ex Marina, Scheldepoort-87, Scheldepoort 2-85, Rammekens-64)

SEA GRIFFON 1962 117 26,85 7,35 3,18 800 14.0
Laid up in Dundee

ST OLAF 1956 37 17,06 4,80 360 4.5

TOWARD VENTURE (ex Margaret Isobell) *Based at North Queensferry*	1969		13,90	3,70	1,80	240	
VELOX *Based on the River Medway*	1949	20	12,60	3,70		110	

The MULTITUG II lies alongside at Yarmouth, Isle of Wight, on 17 February 2004.

(Bernard McCall)

The following vessels are in private ownership

IONIA (ex St Mawes-05, Ionia-88) *Laid up at Bideford*	1960	187	30,41	7,98	3,53	1000	20.0
ODIN			12,19	3,65		325	
THOR			12,65	3,43	1,50	254	2.5

The following vessels are also in private ownership

GARRY GRAY (ex Gary Gray, Lighterman-77, Jaycee-62) *Based on the Holy Loch*	1954	37	18,26	5,00	1,80	325	5.5
ST. BUDOC (ex Foylegarth-83, Foylemore-69) *At moorings in the Holy Loch*	1958	208	31,55	8,46	3,59	1270	18.0
SUSIE B (ex Mainpull)	1954	49	19,80	5,50		300	

GIBRALTAR UNDERWATER CONTRACTORS LTD (GIBUNCO)
Waterport House, PO Box 51, Waterport, Gibraltar
Tel : +350 70454   Fax : +350 79065

SEALYHAM (GIB)	1967	152	28,67	7,39	3,66	1320	16.1

Marine services at Gibraltar

M H BLAND & CO LTD
Cloister Building, Market Lane, PO Box 554, Gibraltar
Tel : +350 79478   Fax : +350 71608
E-mail : shipping@mhbland.gi

FLYFISH (GIB)	1969	77	22,30	6,40	3,00	659	6.0

(ex Edith-95)

Towage and marine services at Gibraltar

STRAITS TOWING CO LTD
PO Box 751, 9/1 North Mole, Gibraltar
Tel : +350 52500   Fax : +350 46290

STRAITS I (VCT)	1970	143	25,30	7,62	3,00	1320	18.0

(ex Hasenburen-98)

Formerly in the fleet of Alexandra Towing, the SUN SWALE is now based in Gibraltar where she was photographed on 15 January 2003.

(John Southwood)

T P TOWAGE CO LTD
PO Box 801, Berth 11, North Mole, Gibraltar
Tel : +350 41912   Fax : +350 43050
E-mail : towage@gibnyney.gi

MUMBLES (GBR)	1969	302	34,00	9,50	3,70	2190	40.0
SUN SWALE (GIB)	1968	192	28,22	8,02	4,40	1500	18.0
(ex Clairvoyant-81)							
EGERTON (GIB)	1969	193	29,01	8,51	4,50	1500	18.0
(ex Subtil-91)							

TUGS - REPUBLIC OF IRELAND

BLUE OCEAN MARINE
Ferry Lodge, County Cork, Republic of Ireland
Tel : +353 27 75009   Fax : +353 27 75000
E-mail : biferry@eircom.net
Website : www.berewislandferries.com

CAVA LASS	1975	15	11,93	3,58	1,20	300	3.0
RYSA LASS	1975	15	11,93	3,58	1,20	348	3.5
ADA DOROTHY	1971	54	20,50	7,01	2,50	343	5.0

Line handling services at Leahill Jetty, Adrigole and Bantry oil terminal; also salvage services

C. W. SHIPPING CO LTD
Fountain Cross, Ennis, County Clare, Republic of Ireland
Tel : +353 65 29470   Fax : +353 65 28316

SHANNON ESTUARY I	1956	176	30,18	8,21	3,12	1040
(ex Scotscraig-86, Flying Duck-76)						

PORT OF CORK COMPANY
Custom House Street, Cork, Co, Cork, Republic of Ireland
Tel : +353 21 273125   Fax : +353 21 276484
E-mail : info@portofcork.ie
Website : www.portofcork.ie
Livery - Light blue hull with white housing and white funnel

DENIS MURPHY	2004	110	18,70	8,00	1,75	960	12.4
GERRY O'SULLIVAN	1996	338	29,50	11,45	2,50	4100	40.0
THOMAS F. DOYLE	1979		16,00			200	

Harbour towage at Cork

DUBLIN PORT COMPANY

Port Centre, Alexandra Road, Dublin 1, Republic of Ireland
Tel : +353 1 8550888   Fax : +353 1 8557400
E-mail : info@dublinport.ie
Website : www.dublinport.ie
Livery - Black and grey hull with buff housing and wheelhouse

BEN EADER	1973	198	29,11	9,35	2,28	1620	16.0
CLUAIN TARBH	1992	268	30,00	9,30	5,20	3440	36.5
DEILGINIS	1996	335	29,50	11,00	3,40	3430	37.4

Harbour towage at Dublin

The CLUAIN TARBH in her home port of Dublin on 10 August 2003.

(John Southwood)

GALWAY HARBOUR COMPANY

Harbour Office, New Dock, Galway, Republic of Ireland
Tel : +353 91 561874   Fax : +353 91 563738
E-mail : galwayharbour@eircom.net
Website : www.galwayharbour.com

LOC LURGAIN II	1970	17	12,65	3,35	1,50	380	1.2
(ex New Ross I)							

Towage and pilot launch services at Galway

HELLEBORE LTD

Bilberry, Waterford, Republic of Ireland
Tel : +353 51 82224   Fax : +353 51 74372
Livery - Black hull with buff housing and white wheelhouse
Managed for Bilberry Shipping

ADEPT	1971	51	17,40	6,30	2,30	580	6.0
AGILE	1971	51	17,40	6,30	2,30	580	5.8
(ex Alerte-78)							
BARGARTH	1960	151	28,90	7,60	3,20	850	17.0

CHRISTINE	1966	77	22,00	6,50	2,50	659	6.0
INGLEBY CROSS	1967	139	26,52	7,68	3,60	1200	12.0

(ex Anglian Man-95, Gunnet-90)

Towage and marine services at Waterford

IRISH MAINPORT GROUP
Monahan Road, Cork, Republic of Ireland
Tel : +353 21 4317900   Fax : +353 21 4311269
E-mail : info@mainport.ie
Website : www.mainport.ie
Livery - Dark blue hull with white housing; dark blue funnel with white company logo,
Operated by Celtic Tugs Ltd

CELTIC BANNER	1982	282	32,85	9,50	3,23	3500	45.0

(ex Take Maru No.78-00, Mikawa Maru-98)

CELTIC ISLE	1986	411	34,20	10,50	4,78	4000	53.6

(ex Tai O-00)

CELTIC REBEL	1984	198	31,20	9,01	4,09	3400	48.0

(ex Take Maru No.71-00)

Towage on the River Shannon and offshore services in the Irish Sea
Operated by Fastnet Logistics

FASTNET FALCON	1961	151	29,60	7,95	3,18	1000	18.0

(ex Abeille No.18-00)

LEE TOWAGE LTD
5 Victoria Estate, Carrignfoy, Cobh, County Cork, Republic of Ireland
Tel/Fax : +353 21 81303
E-mail : leetowag@go.free.indigo.ie
Website : www.ostensjo.no
Livery - Navy blue hull with light blue housing; navy blue funnel with white band and company logo

ALEX	1995	397	30,80	11,65	4,78	4004	50.0

(ex Atlantic Fir-97)

Towage at Cobh and Whitegate

MARINE TRANSPORT SERVICES LTD
Atlantic Quay, Cobh, County Cork, Republic of Ireland
Tel : +353 21 811485   Fax : +353 21 21812645
Livery - Red hull with white housing and light blue funnel with red trim

BREEDBANK	1969	253	33,23	9,20	4,60	2800	30.0

(ex Canada-79, Breedbank-76)

OYSTER BANK	1960	161	28,86	8,39	3,80	1260	17.0

(ex Oyster Bay-95, Totland-93, Europabank-82, Europa-73)

Towage at Cork and Cobh

SHANNON WORKBOATS

Boolsglas Askeaton, Limerick, Republic of Ireland
Tel : +353 61 392419   Fax : +353 61 392410
E-mail : mjkehoe@eircom.net

TORBAY ENDEAVOUR	1975	27	15,75	4,90	2,70	295	4.5

Marine services on the Shannon estuary

SINBAD MARINE SERVICES LTD

Shore Road, Killybegs, County Donegal, Republic of Ireland
Tel : +353 74 9731417   Fax : +353 74 9731864
E-mail : info@sinbadmarine.com
Website : www.sinbadmarine.com

TRIJNIE	1976/99	38	14,45	4,90	1,60	900	9.0
(ex DMS 1494-77)							
NOMAD	1972	91	23,70	7,00	2,60	565	8.5
(ex Duke of Normandy-05)							

Towage and marine services in the Killybegs area

SOUTH EAST TUG SERVICES LTD
(CATHERINE O'HANLON CANTRELL)

19 Otteran Place, South Parade, Waterford, Republic of Ireland
Tel : +353 51 852819 or +353 86 1727502
E-mail : setugs@eircom.net

TRAMONTANE	1972	263	31,63	8,80	4,80	2500	30.0
(ex Marsellais 16-89)							

Towage services on the east coast of Ireland and charter work

*The **TRAMONTANE** has worked in various ports on the south coast of England during 2004/05. She is seen here at work in Falmouth on 25 July 2004.*

(John Brownhill)

INDEX OF VESSEL NAMES

Current names are in CAPITAL letters; previous names are in lower case.

Name	Page	Name	Page	Name	Page
Cam Guardian	6	Copar	74	DHB DAUNTLESS	37
Cam Protector	7	Coral	6	DHB DOUGHTY	37
Cam Ranger	7	Coral Sea 2	3	Dhulia	65
Cam Retriever	7	CORRINGHAM	70	Diamante	74
Cam Searcher	7	COULMORE	50	DIDO	26
Cam Seeker	7	CRAMOND	69	DMS Eagle	29
Cam Sentinel	7	Cromarty Service	6	DMS 1494	81
Cam Supporter	7	Cromarty Shore	6	DONNA McLOUGHLIN	52
Cam Vedette	7	Cromarty Tide	6	Doris	58
Cam Vigilant	8	Cruiser	64	DORIS K	58
Cam Viking	7	CULTRA	69	Drive Supporter	6
Cam Viper	8	CUMBRAE	56,57	Droit de Parole	19
Cam Viscount	8	Curlew	71	Drot	17
Cam Voyager	8	Cyclop	39	DUCKETT	64
CANADA	22	DALEGARTH	68	DUKE OF NORMANDY	48
Canada	80	Dalegarth	39	Duke of Normandy	81
Canmar Teal	15	Dalmatian	58	Dunelm	41
Canmar Widgeon	15	DALMENY	69	DUNTER	61
Canso Dart	7	Daphne	71	Durdham	30
CAPABLE	60	Daphne B	71	Earl	5
CAPT. I. B. HARVEY	73	DAVID ANDREWS	40	Edda Atlantic	12
CAREFUL	60	DAVID McLOUGHLIN	52	Edda Fjord	10
Carew Castle	55	Dawn Patrol	3	Edda Sprite	12
Cariboo	19	Dawn Shore	3	Edith	77
CAROL JAMES	30	De Hoop	6	Eduard	27
CARRICKFERGUS	69	DEA ARGOSY	15	EGERTON	78
CARRON	66	DEA CAPTAIN	15	EILEEN	40
Caspar C	38	DEA CHALLENGER	15	EINAR	56
CASTLE	5	DEA CHAMPION	15	El Marzouk	46
CASTLE POINT	70	DEA CHANCELLOR	15	Elena B	55
Caswell	65	DEA COMMANDER	15	Eldergarth	68
CAVA LASS	78	DEA CONQUEROR	15	ELIZABETH McLOUGHLIN	52
CELTIC BANNER	80	DEA FIGHTER	15	ELKHOUND	59
CELTIC ISLE	89	DEA HUNTER	15	Elsie	67
CELTIC REBEL	80	DEA LINGUE	15	Emerald Bas	12
Celtic Warrior	68	DEA MARINER	15	Emerald Sand	16
Chain Supplier	15	DEA ODYSSEY	15	Emerald Sprite	12
CHALLENGE	37	DEA PILOT	15	EMS Express	49
Challenger III	13	DEA PROTECTOR	15	En Avant 9	44
Chek Chau	24	DEA RANGER	15	ERLEND	56
Cherdas	73	DEA SAILOR	15	Essex Service	3
Chief	26,43	DEA SCOUT	15	Essex Shore	3
CHIEFTON	26,43	DEA SEARCHER	15	ESTE	65
CHRISTINE	80	DEA SEEKER	15	Eston Cross	67
City of Aberdeen	18	DEA SERVER	16	Europa	80
Claire	46	DEA SERVER	16	Europabank	80
Clairvoyant	78	DEA SIGNAL	16	Evans Tide	6
CLEVELAND CROSS	66	DEA SKIPPER	16	Evelene Brodstone	49
Cleveland Endeavour	72	DEA SOUND	16	F. T. Hewlett	7
Clonmel	64	DEA SUPPLIER	16	FAITHFUL	60
CLUAIN TARBH	79	DEA SERVER	16	Falderntor	11
Clutha	56	DEA SUPPORTER	16	Far Baronet	6
CLWYD SUPPORTER	9	DEBEN	24	FAR CENTURION	8
COATHAM CROSS	66	DEBORAH	26	Far Earl	5
COBHAM	24	DEERHOUND	59	Far Malin	11
COLERAINE	68	DEFENCE	50	FAR SALTIRE	8
Collie	09	Deft	24	FAR SCOTIA	8
COLLIE T	69	DEILGINIS	79	FAR SCOTSMAN	8
COLLINGWOOD	23	DEIRDRE	69	FAR SEA	8
Comar	54	DEIRDRE McLOUGHLIN	52	Far Searcher (1975)	12
Comet	39	DENIS MURPHY	78	Far Searcher (1985)	6
Condor	42	DERWENT	74	FAR SERVER	8
Condor IX	42	DEXTEROUS	60	FAR SERVICE	8
CONFIDENCE	33	Dextrous	24	FAR SKY	9
CONSERVATOR	48	DH Alpha	51	FAR SPIRIT	8
Conservator	56	DH Charlie	51	Far Spirit	8

Name	No.
FAR SUPERIOR	8
FAR SUPPLIER	8
FAR SUPPORTER	8
FAR SWAN	9
FAR SWIFT	9
FAR VISCOUNT	9
FARSET OF BELFAST	40
FASTNET FALCON	80
FELAURA	74
Felicity	26
FELIX TOW	36
Felix-Tow	36
FENCER	32
FENLANDER	40
FIDRA	41
FIERY CROSS	66
Filip	26
FLAT HOLM	33
Flat Holm	33
FLORENCE	60
FLYFISH	77
FLYING CHILDERS	75
Flying Demon	41
Flying Duck	78
FLYING SCUD	72
FLYING PHANTOM	68
FLYING SPINDRIFT	66
FORAGER	66
FORCEFUL	60
Fort Reliance	19
Forth (1964)	41
Forth (1979)	67
FORTH BOXER	29
FORTH CONSTRUCTOR	29
FORTH DRUMMER	29
FORTH ENGINEER	29
FORTH FIGHTER	29
FORTH INSPECTOR	29
Foylegarth	76
Foylemore	76
FRANCES	60
Frances	66
Frederick Oldridge	72
FREIGHT ENDEAVOUR	36
FRISTON DOWN	42
Fuji Maru	49
FURNESS ABBEY	25
G.W. 226	58
Ganges	50
GARGANO	11
GARRY GRAY	76
Gary Gray	76
GARY JAMES	30
Gavina (1971)	7
Gavina (1975)	8
Geeste	65
Gemsar	29
General I	71
General V	38
GENERAL VIII	34
GENEVIEVE	60
GEORGINA	60
GERRY O'SULLIVAN	78
GILLIAN KNIGHT	36
GLADSTONE	22
GLENESK	54
Glenesk	52
GLUVIAS	64
Gnupur	7
GOLIATH	64
GRAMPIAN CHIEFTAIN	17
GRAMPIAN CITY	17
GRAMPIAN CLANSMAN	17
GRAMPIAN CRUSADER	17
GRAMPIAN DEE	17
GRAMPIAN DEFENDER	17
GRAMPIAN EXPLORER	17
GRAMPIAN FALCON	17
GRAMPIAN FAME	17
Grampian Freedom	18
GRAMPIAN FRONTIER	17
GRAMPIAN GUARDIAN	18
Grampian Guardian	18
GRAMPIAN HAVEN	18
GRAMPIAN HIGHLANDER	18
GRAMPIAN HUNTER	18
GRAMPIAN MONARCH	18
GRAMPIAN ORCADES	18
GRAMPIAN OSPREY	18
GRAMPIAN OTTER	18
GRAMPIAN PIONEER	18
GRAMPIAN PRIDE	18
GRAMPIAN PRINCE	18
GRAMPIAN PROTECTOR	18
GRAMPIAN RANGER	18
GRAMPIAN SPRITE	18
GRAMPIAN STAR	18
GRAMPIAN SUPPORTER	18
GRAMPIAN SURVEYOR	18
GRAMPIAN VENTURE	18
Gray Delta	27
Gray Echo	33
GRAY JUMBO	39
GRAY MAMMOTH	39
GRAY SALVOR	39
GRAY TEST	39
GRAY VIXEN	39,40
Greatham Cross	69
Grey Lash	36
Gryphaea	3
GUARDSMAN	20
Guarne	54
GULTAKIN ASKEROVA	5
GUNDOG	35
Gunnet	80
Gurroung	23
Gute Salvor	6
GUY JAMES	30
Gwendoline	60
GWENDOLINE P	60
G-WIZ	58
Haja	8
Haki	32
Hallarklettur	8
HALLGARTH	67
Hamilton Piper	17
Hamilton Piper 1	17
HAMTUN	24
HARALD	56
Harvest Reaper III	50
Hasenburen	77
HAVEN HORNBILL	45
HAVILA CLEVER	12
HAVILA FAITH	12
HAVILA FAVOUR	12
HAVILA FORCE	12
HAVILA SEA	12
HAVILA SEARCHER	12
HAVILA SKY	12
HAVILA STAR	12
HAVILA SUN	12
HAVILA TIGRIS	12
Hayakuni Maru	68
HD 91	71
HECTOR READ	75
HELEN	60
Henry Boy	59
HERBERT BALLAM	58
Herkules	22
HIGHLAND BUGLER	9
HIGHLAND CHAMPION	9
HIGHLAND CITADEL	10
HIGHLAND COURAGE	10
HIGHLAND DRUMMER	10
HIGHLAND EAGLE	10
HIGHLAND ENDURANCE	10
HIGHLAND FORTRESS	10
HIGHLAND LEGEND	10
HIGHLAND MONARCH	10
HIGHLAND NAVIGATOR	10
HIGHLAND PATRIOT	10
HIGHLAND PIONEER	10
HIGHLAND PIPER	11
Highland Piper	6
Highland Piper 1	6
HIGHLAND PRIDE	11
HIGHLAND ROVER	11
HIGHLAND SPIRIT	11
HIGHLAND SPRITE	11
HIGHLAND STAR	11
HIGHLAND VALOUR	11
HIGHLAND WARRIOR	11
Hispania	48
HOLMGARTH	67
HOPETOUN	69
Hornbeck Baronet	6
Hornbeck Coral	6
Hornbeck Earl	5
Hornbeck Integrity	6
Hornbeck Sapphire	6
Hornbeck Scout	6
Hornbeck Searcher	6
Hornbeck Supreme	6
Hornby	52
HORTON	25
Hozan Maru	63
HUMBER SENTINEL	25
HURRICANE H	67
HUSKY	60
Hydrex II	46
I. B. SMITH	73
IBEX	63
Ibis Five	3
Ibis Six	15
Ibis Two	15
IJsland	49
IMPETUS	60
IMPULSE (1993)	61

Name	No.	Name	No.	Name	No.
MCS Menno	42	Normand Ondour	15	Plym Echo	33
MCS NIKKI	51	Normand Providence	18	Polar Fjord	18
MEECHING	72	Normand Skipper	16	Polgarth	26
MELTON	22	Normand Trader	16	POLMEAR	41
Mercedes II	53	Normand Vibran	15	PORTGARTH	67
Medway	32	Norse Tide	6	Portnahaven	18
MEDWAY OTTER	53	North Breeze	12	PORTOSALVO	11
MERIT	24	NORTH PRINCE	11	PORTWEY	64
MERLIN	54	North Safe	18	Power Express	15
MERSEY ONE	53	NORTH STACK	46	POWERFUL	60
MERSINA	34	NORTHERN CANYON	21	Prestwick	55
MICHAEL FRANCIS	38	NORTHERN CHASER	21	Pride	30
MICHAEL McLOUGHLIN	52	NORTHERN MARINER	21	PRIMROSE	36
Midgard I	65	NORTHERN QUEEN	21	PRINCE ROCK	31
Mikawa Maru	80	NORTHERN SUPPORTER	21	PRINCETON	44
MILLGARTH	62	NORTON CROSS	68	Protector	71
Minase Maru	63	NOVA	3	Pullman	59
Mirjam	46	Nuna	6	Pushdale H	31
Mohamed	3	O. D. R. 3	17	Pushycat	56
Mona Viking	21	OAKGARTH	68	PUSHY DEV	72
MONARCH M	28	Ocean Coral	6	PUTFORD ACHATES	3
Montenovo	68	Ocean Fighter	17	PUTFORD ACHILLES	3
Moon Lady	3	Ocean Pilot	15	PUTFORD AJAX	3
MOURNE SHORE	35	Ocean Range	12	PUTFORD APOLLO	3
MOURNE VALLEY	35	Oceanic Pioneer	10	PUTFORD ARIES	3
Muhammed Ali	15	Oddstein	15	PUTFORD ARTEMIS	3
MULTITUG II	75	ODIN	76	PUTFORD ATHENA	3
MUMBLES	78	ODS Manta	15	PUTFORD ENTERPRISE	3
MURIA	42	Offshore Hunter	15	PUTFORD GUARDIAN	3
Myrefisk III	18	Offshore Trader	16	PUTFORD PROTECTOR	3
Myrevag	18	Oil Challenger	13	PUTFORD PROVIDER	3
MYRTLE	61	Oil Randan	57	PUTFORD PUFFIN	3
Nagato Maru	63	Oil Retainer	34	PUTFORD ROVER	3
Nancy	47	OLIVER FELIX	25,26	PUTFORD SHORE	3
NAPIA	42	OM	5	PUTFORD TERMINATOR	3
Neftegaz 11	5	Omar	54	PUTFORD TRADER	3
Neftegaz 12	9	ORMESBY CROSS	66	PUTFORD VIKING	3
Neftegaz 58	5	ORSETT	36	PUTFORD VOYAGER	4
Neftegaz 62	5	OTTERBANK	50	PUTFORD WORKER	4
Neftegaz 64	5	OXCAR	41	R~2	8
NERCHA	5	OYSTER BANK	80	R~4	8
NEW ROSS 1	31	Oyster Bay	80	R~5	12
New Ross 1	79	Pallion	64	RACIA	42
Niger	32	Pan Engineer	6	Raiti	8
NIMBLE	60	Pan Salvor	6	Rammekens	75
NIPASHORE	26	Pan Searcher	12	RECRUIT	34
NOLEEN McLOUGHLIN	52	Patmore	51	RED COUNTESS	71
NOMAD	81	PATRICIA McLOUGHLIN	52	RED EMPRESS	70,71
Nor Truck	15	PEARL	19	Red Sea Trader	17
NORAH	26	PENDENNICK	41	REDBRIDGE	25
Nordcap	8	Peng	23	Redcliffe	23
NORE CHALLENGER	54	Peng Chau	23	REGAIN	34
NORE COMMODORE	54	PERCUIL	39	Regard	42
NORE CREST	54	Peter Leigh	30	REGARDER	42
NORE SWALE	55	PHOENIX CROSS	66	REGIS II	33
NORE TRITON	55	Pieter Goedkoop	42	Rem Searcher	12
Norfolk Service	3	Pindarus	17	Remberiturm	12
Norfolk Shore	3	PIONEER	55	Repulse	34
Norindo Star	17	Placard	36	Rescue K	8
Norindo Supplier	17	Placer	36	Rescue Kim (623 gt)	8
NORMAN	63	Plan Searcher	12	Rescue Kim (579 gt)	12
Normand Carrier	15	Plankton	36	Rescue Olav	8
Normand Conger	15	PLANTER	29	RESOLVE	34
Normand Engineer	6	Planter	29	RETAINER	34
Normand Gard	15	Plasma	65	REVENGE	42
Normand Hunter	15	Platoon	65	RICHARD HART	42

Rig Mate	3	Selco Supply 1	3	STACKGARTH	67
RIVERMAN	63	Selco Supply II	15	Stad Flex	11
Rollanes	18	Senho Maru	68	Stad Scandia	18
ROSEBERRY CROSS	66	Senja	8	Stad Spirit	8
Rossinant	15	Sentinel Cathinka	7	Standby Pioneer	18
ROWANGARTH	66	Sentinel Maria	7	Standby Pride	18
Royal	15	Sentinel Teresa	7	Standby Protector	18
RUFUS CASTLE	58	Sentry Hemne	7	STANECHAKKER	61
RYSA LASS	78	SERVICEMAN	63	STANFORD	70
S.B.1	33	SETTER	61	Star Altair	3
Sable Sea	20	Severn Mariner	3	Star Aries	3
Sabrina	42	SHAKESPEARE	51	Star Capella	3
SAFE TRUCK	11	SHALDER	61	Star Pegasus	3
Safe Truck	3	Shalldo	56	Star Spica	16
SALUKI	61	SHANNON	68	Star Vega	3
Salud	32	SHANNON ESTUARY 1	78	STATESMAN	20
SALLY	40	SHEEPDOG	61	Stedingen	65
Salvageman	48	SHETLAND SERVICE	6	Stella Salvator	15
SAMUEL F McLOUGHLIN	52	Shetland Shore	6	STEVEN B	27
Sandhaven	18	Shielwood	17	Stirling Altair	3
SANDSFOOT CASTLE	58	Shinano Maru	63	Stirling Aries	3
Sandsfoot Castle	55	SHIREEN S	67	Stirling Capella	3
Sape	6	Shoalworker	51	Stirling Dee	4
Sapphire Tide	6	SHORNE	24	Stirling Elf	18
Sapucala	6	SHOVETTE	36	Stirling Esk	3
SARAH D	72	SHROVE	50	Stirling Fyne	10
Sarah D	27	Siddis Mariner	3	Stirling Imp	17
SARAH GREY	33	SILEX	63	Stirling Iona	12
SARAH McLOUGHLIN	52	SILVERBEAM	53	Stirling Islay	5
SBS CIRRUS	19	Silverbeam	53	Stirling Jura	5
SBS NIMBUS	19	SIR AUBREY	42,43	Stirling Merlin	18
SBS STRATUS	19	SIR BEVOIS	25	Stirling Osprey	18
Scheldepoort	75	SIR MICHAEL	73	Stirling Puck	18
Scheldepoort 2	75	Sira Supporter	6	Stirling Spey	12
Schnoorturm	20	Skelton Cross	69	Stirling Spica	16
Scotscraig	78	Skorpo	63	Stirling Sprite	18
SCOTT GUARDIAN	6	Smit Amerika	71	Stirling Tay	12
Scott Protector	15	SMIT ARROL	62	Stirling Vega	3
Scout	6	SMIT BAKER	62	STRAITS 1	77
SEA CHALLENGE II	27	Smit Barracuda	3	STRATHDOON	58
SEA ENDEAVOUR	66	Smit Bison	51	Strongbow	68
SEA GRIFFON	75	SMIT FOWLER	62	Subtil	78
Sea Guardian	21	Smit Manta	20	Suffolk Conquest	5
Sea Sapphire	15	Smit-Lloyd 41	15	Suffolk Harvester	5
Sea Serv Osprey	18	Smit-Lloyd 47	15	Suffolk Mariner	21
SEA TROJAN	46	Smit-Lloyd 57	15	Suffolk Monarch	5
Sea Worker	21	Smit-Lloyd 62	20	Suffolk Supporter	21
Seaboard Coral	6	Smit-Lloyd 71	15	Suffolk Warrior	6
Seaboard Integrity	6	Smit-Lloyd 73	15	SUN ANGLIA	24
Seaboard Sapphire	6	Smit-Lloyd 105	16	SUN LONDON	39
Seaboard Scout	6	Smit-Lloyd Sound	16	Sun Mercia	22
Seaboard Supreme	6	SPANIEL	61	Sun Prince	11
Seacor Argosy	15	SPEEDWELL	30	SUN SURREY	24
Seaforth Baronet	6	Sprite	12	SUN SUSSEX	24
Seaforth Centurion	8	SPURN HAVEN II	8	SUN SWALE	77,78
Seaforth Monarch	8	ST BUDOC	76	Sun Tender	12
Seaforth Viscount	9	St David	5	SUN THAMES	24
SEAHAM PRIDE	50	St Cluvias	64	Sun Wrestler	20
SEAHORSE	74	St Jasper	6	Sun XXIII	42
SEAHORSE SUPPORTER	19	St Lucia	8	Sunbas	12
SEAL CARR	41	ST MARGARET	59	SUNCREST	42
SEALYHAM	77	St Mawes	76	Sunset Baronet	6
SEAPORT ALPHA	44,45	ST OLAF	75	Sunset Earl	5
Seaquest Valiant	7	St Patrick	8	Sunset Searcher	6
Searcher	6	St Phillip	8	Sunwind	42
Seaway Jura	3	ST PIRAN	39	Superbe	54

Supreme	6	TOISA VIGILANT	20	VIKING VIGILANT	8
SUSAN	26	TOISA VOYAGER	20	VIKING VIPER	8
SUSIE B	76	Toisa Widgeonl	15	VIKING VISCOUNT	8
SVITZER BIDSTON	68	TORBAY ENDEAVOUR	81	VIKING VIXEN	8
SVITZER BOOTLE	68	TORBROOK	56	VIKING VOYAGER	8
SVITZER BRISTOL	67	Totland	80	VIKING VULCAN	8
SVITZER BRUNEL	67	TOWARD VENTURE	76	Vivien Tide	3
SVITZER MILFORD	68	TRADESMAN	63	VOE SERVICE	37
SVITZER MULL	68	TRAFALGAR	22	VOE TRADER	37
SWAN	5	TRAMONTANE	81	VOE VENTURE	37
Sydfonn	13	Tregarth	56	VOE VIKING	37
SYLVESTER	29	TREGEAGLE	41	Volharding 12	42
TABRIKI	51	TRIJNIE	81	W J Trotter	23
Tai O	80	TRIMLEY	22	Waglan	63
Tai Tam	63	TRIO	56	WARRIOR	71
Take Maru No. 71	80	Triumph Sea	15	Warrior	68
Take Maru No. 78	80	TROJAN	56	WARRIOR III	68
TARROO USHTEY	47	TRUEMAN	63	WATERLOO	22
Tayra	51	TS Herkules	22	WAVENEY CASTLE	11
Te Awhina	69	TS 52 Sound	16	Waveney Castle	5
TEIGN C	71	Tugman	36	Waveney Citadel	10
Tem	8	TULPAR	5	WAVENEY FORTRESS	11
Tender Champion	9	TYPHOON	4	WAVERLEY	42
Tender Searcher	12	TYSTIE	61	Wendentor	19
Tenzan	68	UKD Flat Holm	33	WENDY ANN	49
Terese Marie	49	UKD SEAHORSE	73	West Penguin	12
Terra Nova Sea	16	UKD SEALION	73	WESTGARTH	47
Terrier	55	UNICO	57	Wiberg Supplier	6
THOR	76	VALID	58	WILANNE	73,74
Thorngarth	68	Vanoc	71	WILCAT	74
THRAX	63	Veesea	16	WILFLOW	74
TID 43	44	Veesea Pearl	19	WILFREEDOM	74
TID 71	75	Velox	76	WILJAY	74
TID 174	75	Venture Service	6	WILPOWER	74
Tideall	44	Venturer	5	William George	42
Tidewater Integrity	6	VER	38	WILLOWGARTH	68
TIGRILLO	73	VERA LOCKHART	40	Wimpey Seasprite	11
TIOGA B	27	Veronica	49	Wimpey Seawitch	10
TIRRICK	61,62	Vespa	49	Wira Maju	11
TNT Leopard	19	Vic III	73	Wouter Johannis	71
TNT Lion	19	Vic IV	73	WYEFORCE	47
TNT Tiger	19	VIGOUR	31	WYEFUEL	47
TOISA CONQUEROR	20	Vik III	73	Wyeguard	46
TOISA CORAL	20	Vik IV	73	Wyeplay	47
TOISA CREST	20	Viking	55	Wyepress (1944)	75
TOISA DARING	20	VIKING CHALLENGER	6	Wyepress (1968)	26
TOISA DAUNTLESS	20	VIKING CRUSADER	6,7	WYEPULL	47
TOISA DEFIANT	20	VIKING DEFENDER	6	WYEPUSH	47
TOISA INDEPENDENT	20	VIKING ENDEAVOUR	6	WYETOW	47
TOISA INTREPID	20,21	VIKING GUARDIAN	6	WYKE CASTLE	59
TOISA INVINCIBLE	20	VIKING PROTECTOR	7	YARENGA	5
TOISA LEOPARD	20	VIKING PROVIDER	7	YARM CROSS	66
TOISA LION	20	VIKING RANGER	7	Yarra	24
TOISA MARINER	20	VIKING RETRIEVER	7	Yashima	67
Toisa Petrel	15	VIKING SEARCHER	7	Yenikale	60
Toisa Plover	16	VIKING SEEKER	7	YEWGARTH	67
Toisa Puffin	15	VIKING SENTINEL	7	Yokosuka Maru No. 1	68
Toisa Teal	15	VIKING SUPPORTER	7	Yokosuka Maru No. 2	23
TOISA TIGER	20	VIKING VANGUARD	7	Zal 4	44
TOISA VALIANT	20	VIKING VEDETTE	7	Zephyr	55

Back cover : A shaft of sunlight illuminates the ANGLIAN SOVEREIGN against a bleak and wintry Shetland landscape on Christmas Day, 2004. The location is Scalloway.

(Dominic McCall)